confessions of an

ESSEX GIRL

confessions of an

ESSEX GIRL

Becci Fox

PAN BOOKS

First published 2012 by Pan Books
an imprint of Pan Macmillan Ltd, a division of Macmillan Publishers Limited
Pan Macmillan, 20 New Wharf Road, London N1 9RR
Basingstoke and Oxford
Associated companies throughout the world
www.panmacmillan.com

ISBN 978-1-4472-0563-0

3 5 7 9 8 6 4

A CIP catalogue record for this book is available from
the British Library.

Typeset by Ellipsis Digital Limited, Glasgow
Printed and bound by CPI Group (UK) Ltd, Croydon, CR0 4YY

This book is dedicated to
my parents for a lifetime of support,
and to the people of West Essex
for a lifetime of laughter.

Acknowledgements

First off, I'd like to thank myself for all my hard work. Since bones have been broken during the writing of this book, I must also express my deepest gratitude to my truly amazing Essex brethren: my accident-prone bosom buddy KL (still got it), my favourite man 'the Fontos' JF, my rosé drinking wingman PB – who knew we were researching that whole time? Also thanks to Redman for living danger-ously, to MF for his tawdry tales, the Chelmer girls for a lot of laughs and a lot of cork popping, the entire J Family (what a hen do), my East Anglia crew and my publisher Ingrid Connell for her advice and for giving me this oppor-tunity. And special thanks to my mum and dad for putting up with me and moving us to West Essex. See, I told you going out was more important than school.

Contents

Author's Note

Every drama you read about on these pages truly happened to myself, my friends and my family. Some things are so shameless that ALL names have been changed, including my own. As with *The Only Way Is Essex*, this book is scripted reality. A lifetime of events have been crammed into a six-month narrative but each character is a blend of two or more real people. Every beauty salon, club, bar, doggy day spa, sunbed, posh dinner, tight dress, chat-up line, sports car exists. A number of conversations are genuine banter overheard by myself while out and about in West Essex. It's not that I got good hearing, it's just that everyone speaks so loud it's almost rude not to earwig. The rest is just what me and my crew have said, done and seen over the years. Some of it's word for word, some of it's been dramatized for your entertainment. I call it as I see it.

Prologue

So you think you've got us figured out? Essex girl equals tan, teeth and tits. You don't know the half of it. Let me tell you something. While you've been laughing at them lot from *The Only Way Is Essex*, they've been laughing all the way to the bank. And all because some posh producers came along one day and went, 'Crank up the Essex to the max, and . . . action,' and their selected cast became the caricatures we wanted them to be: over-the-top, mouthy and flash.

There's some West Essex folk who are going, 'That's not what we're like.' Well, a good lot of us are, actually, but do you think we get that rich by being that ditzy? My Essex brethren are fun, down-to-earth go-getters who don't take themselves too seriously. So yeah, what you see on TV is a slice of Essex, but it's still not a patch on what I've seen over the years. If it were the real deal, there'd have been a fight outside Sugar Hut by now.

There would have been some cash-in-hand business caught on camera. There'd be more sunbeds than spray-tans. Harry's gay world would be more adventurous than a dinner date round his mum's house. The white powder would be flying left, right and centre. And the sexual conquests would be graphic and detailed, for if there's one thing we excel at, it's telling a story with all the trimmings.

And that's where I come into all this. I thought to myself, *TOWIE* is a bit limited in what it can show because the cast will only admit to so much and there's all those TV regulations to abide by. So I went to these publishers and said, 'If you like, I can write a kind of book version of *TOWIE* with genuine stories.' Since you don't know who I am and I don't know who you are, I can get proper candid on these pages. Saying that, if I do get found out then I'll be blacklisted by every establishment and banished from Essex. But then again it's worth it, because I honestly believe you'll benefit from all I've learnt when it comes to living, working, playing and dating in Essex. I'm not being funny, but I might just improve your life with my WEG wisdom. A WEG is a West Essex Girl, by the way. You have so much to learn!

Don't get me wrong, I'm not going to be bad-mouthing Essex, because I genuinely believe it's the best place to live if you want to make something of yourself. Yes, the social scene can get a bit incestuous and it's got all the politics of the school playground, but you can build yourself up from nothing here and have a laugh while you're at it. It's got what the rest of Britain lacks, and that's self-belief. Showing off is actively encouraged and modesty is a swear word. And the good news is the West Essex dream is yours if you want it. As my dear old dad says, you can live the champagne lifestyle on lemonade money here. All you got to do is act the part and the rest will follow.

The place is proper riddled with opportunists, and good ones at that. It's no wonder that Burnett bloke came up with idea of *The Apprentice* after growing up round here. All he had to do was look out his front door to see the money-spinning going on. I mean, *The Only Way Is Essex* lot aren't sitting back now they've found fame, are they? Yeah, a lot of them have become professional celebrities, but it's the girls who are starting up all the businesses. They're all fucking working it. You don't see the cast from *Made in Chelsea* grabbing the headlines or opening up shops, because they got no hunger to make their own mark. It's just instinctive for us: elbow your way forward, make a name for yourself and then make a killing off the back of it. It doesn't take a camera crew for us to be like that. I really don't get why everyone isn't doing it instead of moaning about recessions and credit crunches. Take matters into your own hands, yeah?

So I suppose what I'm trying to say is that it's a fucking inspiring place to live if you want to better yourself.

That's why Nan and Grandad left the East End in the first place, and look at us now. But things got weird here last summer and I truly blame the *TOWIE* effect – it sent us all a bit funny. I mean, I live the loveliest life. I'm part of the Essex elite, I look good, I've always gone to the right places and I have nice things. And I only choose blokes who treat me right and show me a good time. But the Essexness went into overdrive for me around the time *TOWIE* started filming the second series. Coincidence? I don't think so. If a 24-year-old player like Mark Wright could even think of proposing to Lauren, then the world had truly gone tits-up.

These aren't my memoirs, so I'm not going to bore you with the time Leigh Cole pulled me to the ground by my hair for looking at her boyfriend. Although I don't think many ten-year-olds have experienced that. And this isn't a diary either. Do you think I've got time to write down my thoughts when I roll in at 4 a.m.? So if there are some discrepancies, I apologize now. When you're under the influence, it makes memories a bit fuzzy round the edges, right? But stay with me, because here's the thing. What I am going to do is break a number-one rule in Essex and just cut through all the billy bullshit. We're the best self-promoters in the country, but sometimes we're too good. I was too good and it turns out there is a limit when it comes to affairs of the heart. I thought I could handle anyone, but then one very good-looking, confident, charming racing driver proved otherwise. I was so far out of my comfort zone, it's not even funny. But you know what, I'd do it all again. I'm actually going to quote Mark Wright here, but don't judge me, because it makes sense: 'We're here for a good time, not a long time.' I mean, imagine if I'd said no to the good times and just stayed indoors and watched my *TOWIE* boxset instead? This would be the end of the story.

As we say in Badlands, get involved.

Looking the Part

The place I need to start is the day I met him.

It's weird how you can just go about your business totally unaware you're going to meet someone in a few hours who's going to properly shake your shit up. I mean, I'd had a proper mare of a day with the girls, so perhaps my normal defences were on the blink. Who can say, but I wasn't feeling too bright.

Just to set the scene, we were all in my sister's bridal shop, where I work as a buyer. My best friend Gemma was the bride-to-be, so she was sat down waiting for her five bridesmaids to emerge from the changing rooms, me included. One by one, we trailed out and stood before her like we were in a line-up. The vibe wasn't quite how I'd imagined it. I mean, I had personally selected these Fifties-style coral dresses and people are always begging me to style them, but this lot had a right face on them.

'What's not to like about them?' I asked. I really was getting quite hacked off. 'Coral is bang on trend, plus it makes you look well tanned.'

As soon as I'd seen these dresses two months prior, I'd bought in a job lot because I thought it was a no-brainer and Gem would be sold as soon as she saw them. They were halter-neck and I have great shoulders; they were knee-length and I have great pins; I hate my bottom and thighs, but they were hidden with a netted skirt. Epic win. However, Brooke suddenly revealed she hated coral because she said it clashed with dark hair. Since when? To me, Brooke is like this little China doll (with a tan) that I just want to dress up all the time. She's got these dark, soulful eyes, and a tiny nose and these ridiculously small ears. But don't be fooled by this exterior because the girl bites. I wasn't about to argue with her over the merits of coral.

Gem's sister Karen looked OK except her back fat was spilling out. I suggested she whack on a shrug, so that solved that. Actually, Gem's cousin Paula had the same problem but they both wear so much make-up I doubt anyone would have been looking below their necklines. It's like they use a face stencil, their tide-marks are so perfect. And in my opinion, Gem's mate from college, Emily, looked amazing, but I couldn't please her either. She said the look was 'a bit much'. She's not a native. I think she's from Sussex. Maybe Suffolk? Surrey? Anyways, she was one of those vanilla girls who badly needed some Essex razzle-dazzle in her life.

'Fuck it, I can't be dealing with all this,' Gemma screamed at us. 'This is the sixth shop we've been in and I've had one hundred per cent grief from all of you. This was *meant* to be fun.'

And it was fun at first. Gem told us each to pick a bridal shop and then she'd choose a bridesmaid's dress for us all to try on. Naturally, I chose the family business, not out of pure selfishness but because I knew I could cut Gem a deal. That's how it works in Essex – never pay full price, use your contacts.

'Becci, considering you're the buyer for this shop, you haven't got a very wide selection. Why is everything above the knee?' Gem said, tossing her long blonde hair in my direction. She's one of those graceful, willowy types who can express a thousand words in just one hair-flick.

This dig at my fashion sense would normally rile me up for a full-on showdown, but not this time. I caught my sister's eye and she busied herself with some papers. That's because Tasha was as guilty as I was, since she'd helped me move all the dresses I didn't like into the stockroom an hour before the girls showed up. I had hoped it wouldn't look too obvious.

'Problem is, Gem, it's March, so everyone's bagged their summer bridesmaid dresses already,' I said in my defence. That wasn't true. I go to wholesalers all the time to replenish stock, otherwise we wouldn't have a business. Duh.

'I suppose I have left it quite late,' said Gemma. I can be quite convincing sometimes. She looked defeated and slumped down on the red velvet chaise longue (it's well plush – chosen by moi) with her head in her hands. I'll fess up, I felt this rush of guilt (there's a first for everything), so I pushed a cold glass of champagne into her hand. That usually livens people up, but she just downed it and walked out the shop. She clearly wanted me to chase her out so I had no choice, which meant everyone outside stopped in their tracks to watch. I felt like saying, 'Wind your fucking necks in, people,' but then that would make me such a hypocrite. I bloody love watching confrontations.

'Look, I've got an idea,' I said, grabbing her shoulder to shake the strop out of her. 'You should give us a colour theme and we'll buy our own dresses. Loads of girls are doing that now, and it makes the wedding party look way more interesting. I'd totally do that myself,' I added, trying to be helpful and selfish at the same time.

'Fine. Just wear what the fuck you all want. Let's just get out of here,' she snapped back. Charming.

This wasn't even our lowest wedding moment. We'd gone to Emily's chosen shop earlier that day and she clearly didn't get how far Chelmsford was for us. That's the thing about outsiders, they don't know how Essex works as a county. All you need to know is that my manor is a cut above the rest. Make us West Essex and them East Essex, I say. We're more urban and classy, whereas Chelmo is hicksville. They all live in the countryside, so they can't help it if their lifestyle expectations are lower. I mean, they rate Dukes as a nightclub and they think a night in Bas Vegas is living the high life. Enough said.

I won't name and shame the shop in case I get in trouble – the bridal business is a small world and I don't want no one giving me evils at the next wedding fair – but let's just say it rhymes with Disgrace. So we go into Disgrace and the boniest bint looks us up and down. Needless to say, she wasn't going to waste her champagne on us. Strike one. We try on a strapless floor-length piece that Emily and Gemma love, but Gem's sister Karen is having issues getting in it. It's a size 16 dress and she's a size 16 (apparently).

The snippy lady goes, 'I would give up on that if I were you. You're clearly a size twenty-two.'

We're all speechless for once. We all turn to Karen fully expecting her to kick off.

'Not according to my jeans,' she says, waving them triumphantly as evidence.

The owner attempts a pinched smile and says, 'Those may be a size sixteen, but bridesmaid dresses are entirely different. Your chest makes you big. I can tell someone's size just by looking at them, and you are definitely a size twenty-two dress.' Strike two.

Karen violently yanks off the dress so there's a faint ripping sound and the woman bristles. But wait, she still has one more blow to serve. She turns to Emily and goes, 'You're a bit older than the average bridesmaid, so if I were you, I wouldn't go for a strapless,' and she displays this sack of a dress.

With gritted teeth, Emily goes, 'I'm only twenty-six.'

To which the owner replies, 'Sorry, dear, it's hard to tell when people have no make-up on.'

To be fair, it is rare to see someone go bare-faced in Essex, and Emily's got such sun-addled skin, and don't even get me started on the hair. Do all people from the shires have straw on their head? Still, I did feel for the girl. We ended up throwing the woman's stupid dresses on the floor, and Brooke shouted, 'What a load of old toot,' as we went. You should have seen the silly cow's face. All outraged.

So now we were back at square one. Still no bridesmaid dresses. I did feel a bit shame-faced, but then if it weren't for me, Gem wouldn't have scored such a bargainous Vera Wang wedding dress. I seriously worked my contacts to sort her out with a designer dress. See, I'm not all bad!

'Gem, we are turning this day around,' I declared as we left Tasha's shop. 'We are going to get ready and then go have the biggest night of our lives. You'll be too hung-over to care or remember you're getting married.' I detected a fraction of a smile. If there's one thing I am good at, it's lifting people's moods. 'Ladies, are you with me?' I said, extending the offer. Turns out they weren't. Excuses of kids and returning back to the sticks were voiced, but that was fine because that meant it was going to be the original crew of me, Brooke and Gemma. Essex was about to witness something pretty special that night, although when we jumped in my car, I still had my doubts about Gem's state of mind, especially when Brooke said, 'Bagsy front seat.' Is it normal for an adult to bagsie things still? It drives us all nuts, but we never dispute her claim. Forced to squeeze into the bucket-seat at the back, Gem went off on one again.

'This car's so stupid. You can't have more than one friend if you drive one of these,' she said, dissing my precious Audi TT.

'Yeah, but wait till it gets hot and we can get the roof down,' I said, ignoring her strop.

'Oh yeah, fucking awesome. You two looking like Thelma and Louise while I'm back here with my legs round my head like Harry bloody Houdini.'

'If you can do that, then no wonder you're the only one with a bloke,' I said. *Finally* she laughed.

'Don't tell Grant I'm so bendy or I'll never hear the end of it. He's been coming out with some right filth lately. Maybe he needs to let it all out before we get married. So you girls going to come over to ours to get ready?'

13

Brooke and I looked at each other in an attempt to read each other's thoughts.

If we were going over to Gem's place in Epping, that meant were going to end up at One9Five, which is literally a stone's throw away. It's the smallest club ever invented, but we've had some top nights there. All very messy. In fact, that's the club we spotted Kimberly Stewart snogging Jude Law in once. How random is that? It was all over the papers the next day because everyone just got their camera-phones out. You can tell Jude Law isn't a local if he thought, 'I'll just go out in Essex for a discreet night out and bang that Stewart girl.' Duh! Her dad must have been so proud of his little princess. If you're a Rod Stewart fan (as if I think he's sexy), just hang out down Epping High Street and you'll bump into him. If you don't see Rod, you'll definitely see Ray Winstone. That said, those boys are probably the cream of the Epping crop, but something told me One9Five was the place to be that night.

'Yeah, go on then,' I say. 'Let's swing by mine first, though.'

'Hun, the night will be over before you get your shit together,' moaned Brooke.

'Oh shush, I'll just throw everything into a bag and we're off. Done and done.'

'Yeah, right,' Brooke said, rolling her eyes. I hate being pigeonholed.

I don't technically live with my parents, but my

bungalow cottage is in their grounds. Dad got the annexe built when my sister wanted to move out, so I inherited it four years ago when she got married. Mum completely redecorated it for me by getting rid of all Tasha's weird monochrome stuff and making it brighter and more glam. The living room has all this gorgeous textured pink-and-white wallpaper throughout and mirrors on every wall. I even got my own red carpet going into the cottage. It's like something from a magazine! She's well into her interior design now, and when people walk into her house, they're begging her to make over theirs. You can't say Jackie Fox doesn't have taste. So I've got my own space but I just walk ten metres for home-cooked meals. Yeah, I'm living the dream.

My baby bro Jake is dying for me to move out, but I know which side my bread's buttered on. I mean, it is a bit shameful for a big strong 24-year-old man to still be living with his parents, but I wouldn't say it's ruined his success with the ladies. Probably because us girls have got used to dealing with mummy's boys round here. I bet you anything he lures women back by telling them he owns this huge house. Dad actually built it! How amazing is that? It looks a lot older than it is with all these olden-day wooden beams and big windows like in churches. Come to think of it, the inside looks a lot like Sugar Hut. And then Mum's well-tended garden backs out onto Epping Forest, which is just stunning. That'll be why I see Jake's birds rubbing their hands together as they leave in the morning. You and the rest of them, love.

There's no pool or tennis court, which I think was a bit of an oversight on Dad's part. Think of all the money I waste on sports club membership, I tell him. When women give him grief like this, he likes to pretend he's tearing his hair out. He should have thought twice before getting married and having two daughters then, shouldn't he.

'You've got five minutes and then we're bashing up the car,' yelled the girls from my baby. I ran into the cottage to give the impression of speed, but I so wasn't going to rush. Five dresses, seven pairs of shoes and one very heavy vanity case later, I struggled out of the door.

'Gem, are your curlers still broken?' I called out.

'Yeah, sorry, they are,' she replied. Urggh, how does she even survive . . . Back indoors I went and dug out my magic curling wand. And some curlers just in case. And some spare hair extensions. I don't really like the clip-on ones as they look cheap, but what's a girl to do if volume just isn't happening?

Next stop was Brooke's crib, which is technically in Woodford but on the road to Chigwell. It's called Repton Park and actually used to be an asylum. Yeah, I know, how creepy is that? There's probably mentalists haunting the health club there. Can I just say, their gym is proper flash if you're looking to join up anywhere. She says it's a really nice community and it probably is now that Jack Tweed's moved out after all the sexual deviance and stuff that went on there. Brooke's loss is my gain since he bloody moved back to my patch in Buckhurst Hill. Can't shift him at all unless he's doing time. I really don't get nice vibes off him when I seen him out, and Gemma despises him. Gem got to know Jade pretty well since they knew a lot of the same people on the West Essex beauty scene. Jade owned that salon Femme Fatale in Loughton and then she opened Homme Fatale nearby because obviously blokes needed their own salon round here.

Gem always said Jade was quite childlike and was proper naïve when it came to people and their agendas. If she married Jack Tweed, that just proves it. Why, oh why didn't she just stick with Jeff Brazier? I've met the bloke a few times and he is genuinely lovely. And Ryan's reported some *very* impressive sightings of Jeff in the men's changing rooms down his gym.

Incidentally, Mark Wright was Jack Tweed's best man, and apparently Mark was desperate for his nan to come to the wedding, but Jade vetoed it because she didn't know the old dear. Yeah, you've got it, that was Nanny Pat. She'd have had no problem getting in now. Jade would totally have been in *The Only Way Is Essex*, no question. There have been attempts to get Jack Tweed into *TOWIE*, but what with him being unlikeable and having a criminal record, producers haven't bitten. Yet.

Brooke was literally in and out of her flat. Impressive

if it weren't for the fact she's an easyJet stewardess so she's got a bag of essentials by the door at all times. But there was more moaning as we crammed in another bag next to Gemma. Most of the time she's the calm and together one of the group, but about once a month, it all comes flooding out and nothing can make her happy. And if I go, 'Are you on your period?' she flips. Today was that day. The only person who can usually get her to lighten up is our old schoolfriend Ryan, but he'd totally bailed on us for some debauchery in Soho. He's only been out for three years, so he's had to make up for lost time by sucking off everyone in sight. If he's out with us on a Saturday night, we've truly been blessed.

It took us nearly an hour to get to Gemma's through all the Saturday traffic. I swear people have watched the phenomenon that is *TOWIE* and think everyone lives in one lovely hedonistic Essex village, but it's a serious mission getting from Woodford to Epping. For those of you that aren't local, this is how it works: Buckhurst Hill, Loughton and Chigwell make up the Golden Triangle. They're a couple of miles from one another, and in my opinion, these places are the epicentre of West Essex. Obviously, that's where I live. Then below the Triangle, you've got Woodford, and way above it, you've got Epping. These places have pretty eventful social scenes too. Obviously we've got the stunning Epping Forest on our doorstep, but the area is pure suburbia, with one high street after another. Then beyond Chigwell, you've got countryside for miles until you hit the mighty Brent-wood. They should build some sort of flyover between the two places because it's a right arse-ache to get to. To be honest, I only go there for Sugar Hut. The people of Brentwood will hate me for shattering the *TOWIE* vision, but there is zero glamour in that town. That's why they don't really do street scenes there. If you don't believe me, just go to Brentwood after spending a day in the Golden Triangle and you'll see what I mean. I just think my manor has a bit more style and class. If they could move Sugar Hut to Loughton, I would be over the moon.

When we got to Gem's, Grant was hard at work painting the front door blue. They'd moved into this place just three months earlier. He actually proposed to Gemma on the day they moved in. She was sat on a cardboard box and he was on one knee. So sweet! But it was the least he could do after all the shit she's put up with. Let's just say he likes the ladies. I suppose you'd call him a pretty boy: a cheeky glint, sparkling blue eyes and a pot of gel in his dark and perfectly coiffed barnet. And I honestly don't think I've ever met anyone more hyper than him.

Apparently Essex is the cheating capital of Britain, but then it also has the lowest suicide rate. That's not coincidence. If you always follow your desires, how are you ever going to be depressed? I actually can't think of anyone who *hasn't* cheated on their partner or been cheated on. If you catch your boyfriend pulling another girl, you give them shit but it's not a deal-breaker. Sex takes it to another level, but even then the majority of the time it doesn't seem to end the relationship.

Even though Grant has been a cheat and can be an irritant, he does have a heart of gold and so does Gem, so they do make a really lovely couple. She won't thank me for saying this, but they're sort of related. Grant is Gem's step-brother's wife's cousin. They might not share blood, but I still find it a bit incesty. Don't come crying to me if your kids have webbed feet, I tell her.

'Watcha, girls, is the foursome tonight? I hadn't pencilled it in my diary,' was the first thing Grant said to us.

Did I forget to add that he's hilarious too? 'Don't worry, Grant, we'll just reschedule it to never,' said Brooke. Sometimes you just have to play along with the silly sod.

'Did you find the dresses you were after?' he asked, not even interested in the answer.

Gem glared at us before saying, 'Not yet, babe. But I think we just need to choose a colour so you and the boys can get going with morning suits and we can get moving with decorations. We can decide that between us tonight, right?' she said, pleading with us.

'Yeah, course,' I replied reassuringly. Only because I knew it was going to be coral.

*

So how long does it take an Essex girl to get ready? Well, three hours if there's only one bathroom. That meant we had to start getting ready at 5 p.m. In fact, if I'm going to be totally honest, three days is standard for the West Essex Girl. You're probably thinking, haven't you got anything better to do with your time? The answer is no. It's good to take proper care of yourself. Anyway, getting ready for a night out is half the fun, even if it does start on Wednesday. Now, I do know what I'm talking about because Mum ran a beauty salon back in the day and I used to work on reception during the holidays, so it's in my blood.

Stage one is preparing the skin for some colour. I'll usually exfoliate on a Wednesday morning before work and I use the king of salt scrubs, Jo Malone Vitamin E Body Treatment Scrub. It costs a bomb, but you won't regret it because it seriously moisturizes your skin too. Then you slap on more moisturizer afterwards. Champneys Body Butter does the job nicely, but it's all about the body oils for me now. I'm quite slippery most Wednesdays. Then, in the evening, more moisturizer.

Never exfoliate, moisturize and tan on the same day. I cannot emphasize this rule enough. It's a rookie error and you're just asking for streaks. If you want your skin in prime condition, you can grease up the next morning but *only* if your spray-tan is in the afternoon. Perfection cannot be rushed.

Queens Road in Buckhurst Hill is the only place to go

if you want a complete beauty overhaul. Chelsea might have the King's Road, but can you shop, slim, tan, paint, glue, colour, tousle, dehair and rehair all within a hundred metres there? Queens Road even has a doggy day spa for my little Marilyn to hang out in. So Thursday lunchtime I get some colour at Belles & Beaus beauty salon. That's the pink salon that Billi Mucklow and her family own. I've been known to go on a Friday if I've been less organized, but *never* get a spray-tan on the day you're going out. You may think I'm a total beauty fascist, but this is serious stuff. You're lucky I'm even imparting the knowledge. You've got to allow a couple of days for the mahogany brown to calm down and the smell to disappear.

The spray-tan itself comes in two shade options: original and dark. Obviously, getting original is wasting everyone's time and money. The darker the tan, the better it looks on Saturday night. I've never gone orange in my life, so guess I'm just lucky/talented in my colouring. Naturally, I have sunbeds too for some tan-on-tan action. I always seek out the ones with German lamps because they're the strongest, apparently. I know the health risks, but when I'm all leathery, dying of skin cancer and still sunning myself at my retirement home on the Costa del Sol, I can look at pictures of me in my youth and know that I couldn't have looked any hotter if I'd tried.

I probably have one sunbed a week for ten minutes, so it's not every day. The one at Belles & Beaus is well slick – the Prestige 990 is like a spaceship. You got your 3D sound station and MP3 dock, you got your mood light, you got your special shoulder tanner. I could go on. They also claim to have 'world renowned' treatments – this is a classic. There is no limit to what you can claim to be and have in Essex. If you don't big yourself up, then no one else is going to do it for you. My other favourite tanning spot is at Room Three in South Woodford. It's only a bloody Power Plate too, so you can tone and tan at the same time. I go there if I've had too many pies. Although Brooke refuses to go there with me now. There was a bit of an incident when a bee got in her booth and she had to burst out in her thong. So yeah, tanning can be dangerous.

Then there are the little additions that give that extra edge: lash extensions. You may think what mug would pay for eyelashes when you can just use mascara? Well, don't knock it until you've tried it. I don't think I've ever been so happy as when I first saw myself after having a full set done. I thought, I look so fucking pretty I could just die right now. I've achieved beauty nirvana. (By the way, I will be throwing in the odd fancy word cos I went to private school, so I can do the upperbrow and lower-brow shit. But don't go thinking it was like Eton. Even Amy Childs went to private school here. Imagine a totally reem Hogwarts where Harry Potter looks like he should be in a Wham!, video while Hermione's always on her pink BlackBerry and trying to catch Ron's attention by rolling up her skirt higher and higher. Jessica Wright was two years below me, so you get the picture.)

Anyways, the lash extensions. You know if you wake up in a new bloke's bed and you think, God, I must look like shit. Well, you *can't* look like shit with lash extensions. You will look glorious even if you're dying on the inside. If you've got a really glam occasion, get yourself a double set.

Then of course there's the hair extensions. We've actually got a specialist extensions salon called Coco on Queens Road which promises to 'Botox your locks'. I've got dead straight hair so I need all the help I can get in that department. I always get real hair wefts (synthetic hair should only be seen on Barbie dolls) and prefer bonds to a weave because it's a more natural finish. You got to pay good money if you want quality extensions, though. Pay cheap, pay twice, that's what Don Fox says. Get the cheap bonds and they just fall out with the smallest tug. Imagine going down on a bloke, his hand rests on your head and then he screams as he holds up a fistful of your hair? Major passion killer. And I wouldn't bother with clip-in extensions either. They always look obvious, and if you get caught in a gust of wind, they flap about like your scalp's coming away. Then there's my hair colour – a full head of blonde highlights every eight weeks. I get my bio-gels done about every three weeks. That's a manicure and pedicure to you, but the colour's practically permanent, so I'm saving money with that one. Apart from having to pay for touch-ups. You won't catch me in acrylics. I hate the feel of them and they look cheap, but Brooke's all over them so I have to keep my opinion to myself.

Let's see, is there anything else? Obviously I had my teeth whitened, but that doesn't require regular sessions. I think you got the picture now, though: looking good is the only way in Essex. If you look the part, you'll meet the right people and life will start happening for you.

So now you know all that, you must be wondering what did I possibly have left to do at Gemma's? I'll tell you what. Firstly, I had to open the champagne. The other two are scared of the cork going in their eyes. Then one by one we trooped into the bathroom, flutes still in the hand and razors at the ready to completely defuzz. Sounds dangerous, but we've been doing this for years.

Oh, there's another thing I've had – hair laser surgery. I'm as bald as a coot. Well, not completely. I still have a landing strip around my noo noo so I'm not completely childlike. (In case you're wondering, no I don't vajazzle. I tried one a couple of years back, what with all the hype. No one really got it done before Amy started vajazzling. But never again. The crystals kept cropping up in the strangest places, and I'm still scared I've absorbed some of them.) So anyway, dehairing isn't an issue any more, which is liberating. Isn't it weird that I'll use extensions to gain hair but then I go to extreme lengths to get rid of hair too? There's no justice in this world.

It takes us about forty-five minutes to do our faces. I always get Gemma to do my eyes since she's the pro and has the steadiest hand in the business. The secret of evening make-up is a shit-load of black eyeliner (MAC Blacktrack every time) and mascara (always Max Factor followed by Givenchy Phenomen'Eyes to separate the lashes. That round wand will change your life). If you go a bit wrong with the eyeliner, just cover it up by putting more on. You can't have enough drama around the eye area. Kate Middleton really stole our daytime look as far as eyeliner's concerned, but that's fine. Imitation is flattery.

Brooke once said to me, 'Do you think I wear too much make-up?' Someone had obviously got to her. So I said, 'What's the point of make-up if you're not having fun with it? It's there to glam up your life.' Also, I've seen her without make-up on. The first time was on a girly holiday when she came out of the shower. I actually fell back against the wall and gasped because I didn't know who she was. Her eyes were so tiny. I felt proper terrible, but you can't hide your reactions.

Another make-up essential is bronzer. I use two – a matte MAC one to contour and a Bobbi Brown Shimmer Brick to highlight. Honestly, it's a real art form. I don't know what people do if they don't have a make-up artist for a friend. They must just have to guess.

Next we do each other's hair, fixing extensions, back-combing it, twisting it, piling it up, running the tongs down it, choking on hairspray. Then we all spritz our-selves with the *TOWIE* fragrance Dazzle (as if! Men have been known to throw up when they catch a waft of that horse piss. My signature fragrance is Agent Provocateur, the original). After that there's the outfit combinations. It can take an hour for us to go through all our options, borrowing shoes, ditching jewellery, adding more. For instance, I'd put on a gold necklace and Brooke went, 'Stick a silver one on too,' which sounded mad, but it was life-changing. Two contrasting necklaces are so much edgier. My top clothes tip is only get ready with friends who are the same size as you. You'll never have an outfit crisis again as everyone will pull together and offer up their clothes until you're looking a hundred per cent. Even though we're all size 10s, the girls are always cursing my 34Ds. I can't help it if they got issues filling up my cups. That's why chicken fillets were invented, for Christ's sake. Or you wear two padded bras. It's me that's got the raw deal when it comes to the frock swop. Some of their dresses clamp me down so tight, I can feel my implants pressing against my spine. Not that I want a deflation option.

I wore a brand new dress that night. Grey and off-the-shoulder with black jewels on the front. The skirt bit was all ruched up around the bum and hips, and two drapes of material hung down the back. And it was a low back, which showed off my favourite asset. Sorry to blow my own trumpet, but my sex was on fire. Oh, and these fab beige shoes from Kate Kuba that are suede with a snakeskin platform and heel. I think you'll agree my look was classy, glamorous and very sexy. The only slutty thing was the tightness of the dress, although I would call that a silhouetting of the curves. It never fails to reel in the admirers.

Brooke went for a long orange-and-blue silk dress with a slit right up the leg. It sounds rank, but totally worked with a tan. Gemma kept it classic with a tight black sequinned dress, but it had a cut-out side panel on one side. Some people don't have the figure for these dresses, and it makes me sick up in my mouth when I see flesh squeezing through these cut-outs. Why don't people know that's just nasty? But Gemma has the flattest stomach ever, so all you could see was her taut golden-brown skin. She looked one hundred per cent smoking hot.

Perhaps too hot, because it kicked off between Gem and Grant. If I remember rightly, it went something like this:

GRANT: 'Darlin', you're not going anywhere looking like *that* without me.'

GEM: 'Shut up, Grant. I'm not going to do anything, am I? I've only got eyes for you.'

GRANT: 'Yeah, and they'll all have their filthy eyes on you. Put a jacket on or go change.'

GEM: 'What? We always go out like this. What do you want me to wear? A bin liner?'

GRANT: 'Nah, because you'd get the bin liner and cut out some holes so your lils can poke out. That diamond ring you're wearing is a symbol of . . . Oi, where's the ring?'

GEM: 'I don't want to lose it, do I?'

GRANT: 'I've heard it all now. You're on the fucking pull.'

What happened next was something I've seen her do before, but it still fascinates me. Gemma just goes over to him, holds his face, strokes his hair and says something quietly. What does she say? She never tells me. She's like the Boyfriend Whisperer. Thankfully, the taxi honked outside. 'See you, Grant. Have a good night,' we yelled as Gemma worked the final stages of her magic. When I made her tell me what was winding him up so much, she went, 'I think he was just jealous because he wants a big night out. He's not used to staying in.'

'Guess he's feeling old now. What with you both engaged and twenty-seven,' Brooke said flippantly. Gem's face was like thunder. She takes everything so personally and hates anybody even suggesting she's getting on. Pretty much every time we're on a dance floor, she'll yell at me, 'STILL GOT IT.' And I just think, 'Issues, hun.' It's probably because I'm still twenty-six and free and single that I can't relate to this.

Course I've still got it. Where would it have gone?

2
Getting the VIP Treatment

I bloody love Nu Bar. I'd actually bullied the other two to go here before going to One9Five, even though it was a cab ride all the way back to Loughton, which is practically next door to my house. I'm not normally such a dictator, but I hadn't been out for ages because of the shitty snow, so I was suffering from major cabin fever. I needed my Nu Bar fix to see who was out and about.

This place gets majorly rammed, but that makes it all the better for getting up close and personal. It's got even crazier since *TOWIE* and queues are snaking round the corner by 10 p.m., so you're an idiot if you don't get there before then. And when I say it gets rammed, about eight hundred people go through their doors on Saturday nights though the place is only the size of my living room. The entrance is the only roomy part of the bar and we always bag the prime spot – to the right of the doors, by the window, perched on three white stools. It's like holding court cos basically anyone we know will come to us as soon as they've come in, and that guarantees us a drink since they're always en route to the bar. And if we clock a hottie we don't know, we can keep tabs on them as soon as they walk in.

Essex is proudly sexist and ageist – to get into Nu Bar, girls have to be over eighteen, but the guys have to be over twenty-one. Young girls make a venue look hotter and men under twenty-one start fights. That's just fact. You get a lot of Spurs players down here, but I'm still waiting for David Bentley to show up. And before you say anything, I know he's on loan to West Ham. WEGs might not watch football, but we follow all the fit players.

It's so easy to pull round here, so you can afford to be properly choosy. Some say I'm too picky, but I'm not going to go after any old bloke. Especially as you have to be careful of bullshitters. Pretty much every bloke says they're a semi-pro sportsman. To me, that means they play golf at the weekend. Mark Wright used to be a semi-pro footballer. You see what I'm saying? A lot of people from school have stuck around the area, but there are a handful that moved to London, and they forget that West Essex is social central. For instance, the fourth member of our group, Cleo, lives in Camden with some girls she met at university. Whenever she comes back home, this is what she always says on a night out: 'Oh my God, everyone's so friendly in here. That girl at the bar just told me she'd give me a half-price manicure at her salon, that bloke over there bought me a drink, and that other bloke is married so he's not on the pull, but he's given me his business card . . .' (Yeah, considering Cleo lives in London, she's well green.) But anyway, my point is that London folk are deprived socially. When we go up west for a night out, our group is rarely infiltrated, and people don't know what to do if you start talking to them. In Essex, I spend the night weaving in and out of people and conversations. If there's someone you like, leave them hanging because there's nothing like a bit of sexual tension and you can always seal the deal with a snog and a grope later. I think everyone's a bit more uptight in London. Just saying. They're all like, 'Oh my God, I just spoke to a new person.'

Also, the quality of men in Essex is so much better. There are a lot of pretty boys who aren't really my type, but there's also a lot of manly men who seriously work out. Although I will say one negative thing. A lot of the guys here shave their chests. Hairy backs are just plain wrong, but I like a rug up front. Ryan always says if I was a gay man, I'd be into bears. Awww, bears! The gays are too cute.

Brooke got in the first round of drinks. Champagne, naturally. She'd done the barman at Christmas so she didn't actually pay. To be honest, with us in the window, we were doing the business a favour. I guess you're thinking we sell ourselves to get the perks, but I don't think Brooke had a bad time when she was taking one for the team.

Just as we were clinking glasses, I felt the room go cold. Bloody Vicki P. had walked in. As expected, she gave us such evils. What I was saying earlier about people being more friendly here – I forgot to add that arch-enemies are the exception to the rule. But they do add a bit of drama to the night, so I guess they have their place.

Vicki P. is this tall, skinny bitch who went to Essex Hogwarts and she is a total Malfoy. She even has the bleach-blonde hair in a pixie-crop which she gels back when she's feeling proper evil. Just because her dad's in some ageing rock band that I've never heard of she reckons she's the dog's bollocks. She's definitely a dick. She doesn't even do a quick cutting glance at you. She'll start the look with your hair, and then she'll slowly work her way down your body, and her eyes look like they're burning with disgust and her nose wrinkles like she's just smelt something bad. It's one hundred per cent chilling. They should take her out to Afghanistan and stick her in terrorist areas so she can glare out with a glass of rosé in one hand and a fag in the other. Those extremists would totally forget about the bombs strapped to their chests and just think, 'Shit, why didn't I trim my beard before I left the cave?'

So anyways, Vicki was managing to give us the look

while talking to the doorman, who is a complete legend – I'll call him Barry the Bouncer, otherwise all the other door guys will get jel if I single him out. Somehow she managed to give us evils while turning on the charm for him. I can't even explain how that's possible, but it's multitasking in its nastiest sense.

'She's something else,' said Brooke, returning the glare. Brooke's spent years trying to dish the look back to Vicki, but it's really difficult. West Essex is like the Wild West sometimes.

'Such a boys' girl,' observed Gemma, and we all nodded our heads and looked away to express our contempt. In our group, there's no worse insult than to be called that. A boys' girl only livens up when there's a bloke she can flirt with, but she has nothing to say to her own kind. In my mind, that means there's something seriously wrong with her. Vicki P. had found one friend to come out with her that night (the mate wasn't a looker, so not a threat), but you knew she'd be ditched as soon as Vicki had pulled. No loyalty. Although it's no good being a girl's girl either, before you start going the other way. You need to be multisex and give everyone your time. Unless they're a complete loser.

By 9 p.m., the bar was a sea of tight dresses and even tighter shirts. When it comes to looking good in Essex, less is more: the less you wear, the more attention you get. There's a shop in Loughton that has this written above the changing room in pink letters: 'Fashion is all about eventually becoming naked.' That pretty much says it all. If you're not being noticed, why do you bother going out, huh?

We got approached by so many blokes that night that aren't even worth mentioning, but I will tell you about the three blokes that made us want to run screaming. I forgot to mention a major problem with Essex men: they are vertically challenged. I don't know what's in the water round here, but five foot six is the average height of an Essex man. They try to make up for it by wearing Cuban heels, but seriously, mate, I can see you're short. And these three munchkins were no exception.

'Alright ladies,' said one with tinted blond tips. He had so much self-assurance he made Simon Cowell look shy. That's the thing – their shortfall makes them cockier. Blondie then takes the ice out of his drink and slams it on the table in front of us so we all jump.

'What the fuck was that about?' screeched Brooke.

'I'm breaking the ice, aren't I?'

How lame.

'Have you been going round the bar all evening doing that?' I asked.

'Nah, you're my first victims,' he replied. The other two just stood there laughing at his every word. He was clearly the ringleader. Nice blue eyes, though.

'Don't I know you from somewhere?' Blondie goes to Brooke.

'Nice one, babe. Do you just speak in chat-up lines?'

'Nah, I do know you. Weren't you the air hostess on the Malaga to Stansted flight last week?'

Brooke looked thoughtful, and then her face dropped.

'Oh yeah, I remember you. You're the bloke who'd just got off working on a yacht. You harassed me.'

'Spot on, darling. I'm going back there in May if you want to join me on my yacht.'

Brooke turned to us and jabbed her thumb in his direction. 'This one is a right wise guy – don't you remember I told you about that nightmare flight?'

There are so many tools on Brooke's flights that it's really hard to keep up.

'The first thing he says to me is, "Alright, love, wanna check me seat belt, do ya?", and then he winks to the lads he's with as he cups his balls. Then he turns round and says, "My mates are telling me to ask if you want to go to breakfast with me? You reckon that's a good chat-up line?" So I say, "Nah, not really." Then I give him his drink and he chucks something down his shirt and goes, "Let's play a game: I've hidden an icecube on my body. You've got to find it." You was non-stop for three bloody hours,' she said, turning back to him. 'And your obsession with ice is just weird, too.'

Blondie properly puffed his chest out with pride.

'If I was a really ugly guy, I wouldn't chat up girls,

would I? Admit it, you enjoyed it. Who's the gobbiest geezer you've ever had on a flight?'

'You.'

'And who's the prettiest? And the fittest?'

Fuck, this guy was something else.

After a few minutes they realized they were getting nowhere, but as we said our goodbyes the bloody photographer came over. 'Can I get a picture of you lot?' he asked, already lifting up his camera. Every bar in Essex has a photographer. It's like having to deal with the paps, which obviously everyone in this room wants. We didn't make any effort to get out of our seats, so we looked like giants hanging out with Dopey, Sleepy and Sleazy. I was just freaking out about it going up on Nu Bar's website. After the weekend, everyone scans the gallery to see who's been there. I could see Vicki P. was bloody laughing it up, the bitch. I monitored the website for a month, but they must have thought the circus had come to town so it never got put up. How lucky was that?

As the tiny fellas walked away (obviously, Blondie couldn't just say a simple 'Bye' and went, 'Thank you. Good Night. Much love' and so on), Brooke turned to us with wide eyes and a pursed mouth.

'They didn't even offer to get us a drink. After all I've had to put up with from that guy. Out-bloody-rageous.'

'Yeah, but then we'd have owed them and they'd have followed us around,' said Gemma.

'Nah, that's not true. We're masters of shaking people off,' Brooke replied. 'Right, no more time-wasters, let's get involved,' and with that Brooke launched herself off the stool – but the back of her dress stayed on the seat, lifting up for all to see two peachy cheeks.

'Whoaarrrrrr . . .' went the crowd. Brooke just raised her arms like an actor lapping up a standing ovation. She's good for getting us noticed like that. I was just relieved she'd worn a black thong. If there's any risk of a VPL, she goes commando. The girl has no fear.

We weaved our way through the people and stood at the corner of the bar with the last few dregs of our drinks. It didn't take long for some blokes to get the drinks in. Just as we were planning to make a strategic manoeuvre over to a couple of fitties by the DJ, I heard a familiar voice. 'Becci, what you doing here?' I turned around thinking what a dumb question, to find my cousin Russ stood there. Let's just say the brains of the family don't come from my mum's side. Bless him, he reminds me of an excitable puppy sometimes. It's the way he bounds up to you all wide-eyed, his tongue lolling to one side. He's as skinny as a whippet too – it's all that nervous energy. But what I wouldn't do for Russ' cheekbones.

'Hun, why wouldn't I be here?' I reply.

'I thought you were on holiday.'

'What you talking about?'

'That's why you couldn't come to my big club night up west. That's what you said.'

I had been majorly busted, so I had to cover one lie with another. No other option.

'Oh yeah, I was going on holiday, but then Tasha got ill so I had to run the shop this week.'

'Shit, hope she's OK.'

Lying to drunk people is ideal. If you're caught out later, deny the conversation ever happened and make out they're losing the plot.

'Oh yeah, she's fine now. She just had stuff coming out both ends so she couldn't be near them wedding dresses.'

'But then you still could have come last night.'

'Yeah, but I thought I was going on holiday, didn't I, so I didn't put it my diary. Sorry, doll. But where's your other half anyway?' By this, I meant Rob. They do every-thing together. Apparently they're not gays.

'Rob's having a slash.'

I was about to make some snide comment about cottaging (Ryan has taught me so much) when Brooke rocked up with a bottle of champagne and a well buff bloke in tow. Sweet as. She turned to my cousin and went, 'Oi, Russ, you know *The Only Way Is Essex?*'

'Know it, babe? I'm in it,' said Russ smugly.

'No way!' gushed Brooke. Like we didn't know what with his hourly Facebook updates. 'When were you in it?'

'Last episode. Me and Rob were at the launch party at Minnie's,' he said proudly.

How many times have I heard this story? He claims he said a line which then got cut. How convenient. He probably thinks he's the reason TOWIE got a BAFTA. Brooke's hobby is winding up dickheads, so she couldn't just leave it at that, could she?

'Oh my God, Russ. So you going to be in it again?'

'I should bloody hope so. It's about who you know round here, ain't it, and we're like best mates with Kirk.'

'Shuuuuut up!' screamed Brooke. I spied Rob walking over really fast, which was quite something for him. He has this big, heavy body to haul around so speed is not his forte but he's the most chilled-out bloke you'll ever meet. He's like the yin to Russ' yang. Mentally, they're a match made in heaven. And Rob's had a thing for Brooke for ever. As if!

'Alright, Brooke?' he said, out of breath.

'Hiya, Rob. Oh my God, Russ is just telling me about you two hitting the big time.'

'Well, we don't really like to talk about it, but yeah, and we got more coming up. Filming something for them on Monday.'

'Fucking amazing, Rob. How do you guys fit it all in, acting and all your club nights?'

'You got to take every opportunity thrown at you, ain't ya?'

They were wearing matching checked shirts. You'd think they'd have consulted each other before leaving the house.

'Oh fuck, it's Bucket,' Russ suddenly said, hiding behind me. I look over and clocked Vicki P. I had totally forgotten that was her nickname. How could I? Russ and her went out for about six months when we were nineteen, but she was very accommodating and would give anyone a ride who asked. Anyways, after they broke up, Russ bitterly started calling her Bucket. Turns out she has a cavernous organ. Not my words, his. It's well empowering to find your nemesis's secret shame. From then on, her death stare barely touched me because I'd remind myself that I wasn't the one with a baggy noo noo. I get given a lot of dirt on people, but I also have a sieve for a memory. It's such a cruel combination. I'm just glad I've had the chance to write the name down so it's in black and white for eternity. Sweet justice.

'What you worried about, Russ? You split up seven years ago. You're not still cut up, are you?' Brooke asked, still intent on stirring.

'Fuck off. No, I just don't want her anywhere near me. I might catch crabs again.'

'What? You never told me about that!' I actually went really high-pitched with excitement. I had two things on Bucket now. Joy! What a skanky cow. As predicted, she had two men hanging off her while the 'friend' was standing behind her in a cloak of invisibility. I was so tempted to tell these blokes exactly what they were getting themselves into – literally.

Actually, I probably shouldn't call her Bucket as I'll say it to her face at some point. Also, I know the agony of a nickname. I got one that has stuck like mud. In my promiscuous years, I gave a guy a blowie round the back of Waitrose in Buckhurst Hill. When his friends found out, they started calling me Rosie, as a homage to my supermarket of choice. It's fine if your friends come up with a piss-take nickname, but not some random blokes with a blabbermouth mate. And anyway, he tricked me into doing it because I told him I had a sore throat and he went, 'Well, you know what's good for that, don't you?' I wish I'd just gone home and had a Lemsip instead. It makes me shudder when one of those blokes sees me and yells Rosie in my direction. I was only nineteen – give me a break. At least I've moved up in the blow-job world. Bucket can't do anything about her organs.

'The talent in here is not good tonight.' Gemma had come back over clutching a handful of business cards. That's how an Essex man chats a girl up these days – thrusts his card into her hands. The problem is they're good at self-promotion, but all that glitters is not gold. Like you might meet a property developer and then you sleep with him and see him the next day working the cement mixer on a building site.

'Right, we're totally done. Let's get out of here,' said Brooke with determination.

'Why don't you come to Luxe with us? We'll get you straight in, free drinks,' said Rob desperately.

'I don't think so, babe. It's too packed in there on a Saturday night,' I replied. Truth is, if the talent in Nu Bar is no good then it's not going to improve across the road, because it's the same crowd.

Gem called a taxi and it was there within five minutes. Whoop, whoop, we were off to large it at One9Five, as my sister would say. She's so old-school. Tasha's ancient enough to remember nights out at Epping Forest Country Club. She even claims to have invented a chant which then took the club scene by storm in the mid-Nineties. Poor love, she hangs on to this as she doesn't get out much now with a young kid to look after. Well tragic.

There are three queues at One9Five: the normal queue, the guest list priority queue and the VIP queue. You just don't chance the normal queue. It's so small in there that by 10 p.m. that queue gets told to shove off cos they're at full capacity. But still they queue, the donuts. Guest list is as long as the normal queue, so those at the end don't get in neither. What you want is the VIP queue. It's so VIP, there is no queue. That's why you always get to know the doormen. They're your fast ticket in, but let me tell you, it's taken me a decade of clubbing to get to where I am now.

You have to understand, every business has a VIP level in Essex. It's in our mentality to chase VIP, so it's an obvious way to attract the West Essex punters. But the true VIP is never stated. For instance, guest list *think* they're VIP, but really they're not. And sometimes you'll find a queue and then get inside to find it empty! Gem's step-brother is a doorman at another well-known Essex establishment, and he says they're told to create queues to make a place look more popular. And people get a bigger buzz if they think they've blagged their way in, so everyone's happy.

The other thing Essex is obsessed with is age limits. So I've told you Nu Bar's, and then One9Five is over-21s, but on Fridays it's over-29s. Totally random numbers that mean absolutely nothing if you're an attractive girl. It's just to keep the munters out and all those kids looking for a fight. One9Five actually got shut down because a fight got so out of control. That's why they're now well tough on security. People like Jack Tweed are always chucked out, so it shows the system works.

West Essex also has a proper strict dress code for blokes: no jeans, no gloss designer trainers, no Timberland boots, and they're very specific on canvas footwear. The clubs have had to accept that an Essex boy loves going sockless in his canvas shoes in the summer, so they're banned, but Boxfresh deck shoes and standard boat shoes are acceptable. In my book they're unacceptable, but no matter as they're drowned out by the shoe of choice: the winkle-picker. I think a pointy leather shoe is very *Mad Men*. You can tell a lot by a man's shoes.

I mean, who's going to show you a good time – the bloke in the scruffy boat shoes or the bloke in the shiny points? Trust me, the boat-shoe man does not own a boat. The London types get annoyed by our rigid codes, but it keeps things smart, doesn't it? The way we look at it is, the ultimate club experience is a joint effort. If the club looks flash, we'll look glam in return. All clubs and bars round here aim to bring the West End experience to West Essex. And we're talking Mayfair, not Leicester Square.

One9Five was packed when we got there, but that made no difference to us. Again, it's about who you know, and my ex, Charlie Ferrari, was one of the blokes manning the rope to the VIP Lounge that night. He's done most of the clubs round here and I always get a buzz when I see him as it's guaranteed access to VIP. You might think what's the big deal about VIP, but when you see how crammed a top West Essex club gets, you'll be after the space and special treatment too. Obviously I did a little bit of flirting with Charlie because that's what you do with VIP. It's not strictly necessary with him, since he would have let us in anyway, but I can't help myself when I see him. He works out and he's got that dark Mediterranean look about him but he's nothing amazing to look at. I mean, when I first met him back in the school days, he actually had a pony-tail. Ironically, that's gone and so has the rest of his hairline. This epic fail in the hair department just shows what a good personality he must have. I exaggerate but his forehead does seem bigger every time I see him.

'You're looking proper dapper tonight, hun,' I said.

'Heard you were coming, didn't I?' he replied. 'Thought, better have a shower, put some gel in me hair, look the part.'

'Stop taking the piss,' I said, shoving him in the chest. 'You make out I'm some sort of judger. I take people as they come, hun. At the end of the day, it doesn't matter how trussed-up someone is because the threads don't make a man, right? It's what's underneath that counts.'

'I suppose I have found myself with no clothes on a lot when I've been around you,' he said, to get another smack on the chest from me. 'So what you're saying is, you're impressed I look alright tonight because normally I can't dress myself, but it's alright because I'm so buff underneath it all?'

'Not really, hun, but we'll roll with that.'

'Well, I've never had any complaints from you, so I think that is what you're saying,' he said adamantly.

It's so weird how flirting with Charlie is fun at first, but the banter always turns intimate, almost so he can relive for a split second that feeling of being my boyfriend. See what he did there, ending the conversation with the present tense? That's what I'm talking about. And it leaves me slightly uneasy and a bit confused. Like, we went out for a drink recently and he ordered a vodka-lime tonic for me, which is actually something I don't drink any more, but he likes to make out he knows me inside out, and maybe he does in some ways, but I do have changing tastes, you know. So I wave the barmaid back over and say, 'Actually, can you make that an Amaretto on the rocks,' and Charlie quips to the barmaid, 'She always gets what she wants,' and rolls his eyes like he's the long-suffering boyfriend. We've been split up since 2008! I love him to bits, but he winds me up something chronic.

He's not actually called Charlie Ferrari, but he used to do a lot of coke back in the day and owned a Ferrari. He's scaled down the coke, and the Ferrari is now a BMW, so the name doesn't work really. No matter. Actually, he replaced the coke with steroids, which is the main reason we broke up. That and he's short. And he's a bouncer. Is it so wrong to have aspirations? But them steroids send a man crazy. Yeah, he was looking more bulked-up than ever, but he was always so cross with me. And I just thought, hold on, mate, a short guy's pretty lucky to get with me, so who the fuck do you think you are, putting me down all the time? He did make me laugh a lot, but the anger started to overshadow the good times. He is lovely, though. I'm not being a big-head, but as you can see, he's definitely still into me. Just saying.

The first person we clocked in VIP was bloody Bucket. Her speed is impressive, I'll give her that.

Naturally she was all over some Spurs footballer, but then so were seven others. Apparently, Ashley Cole takes a minder out with him now to beat off all the gold-diggers. Having seen these girls in action, I wouldn't say this is an overreaction. There are so many sex scandals with footballers because it's handed to them on a plate. It's hard not to resist the opportunity.

I have a mate, who shall remain nameless and sex-less, who works in this club, and as soon as I'm in, I ask my Insider who's who and they'll manoeuvre us to the good areas. It's usually in the VIP Lounge, but some-times it's the Black Suite or the VIP Private Room. If I've had to pay for a drink on a night out here, something's amiss. The thing is, big spenders come to Essex to boost their egos. If you got the money to pay for a table in VIP, say around a grand, it will be arranged that you can feel like Hugh Hefner for the night. They also offer tables along the dance floor for people who want to feel like they're VIP but don't quite have the moolah or the con-tacts. It's exactly the same concept as the 'priority' queuing. These people get to feel they're living the VIP lifestyle with their reserved table, but it's honestly not the real deal. People pack their mates into these areas, drinks are spilt and it gets messy. And then you still have to pay a minimum bar tab. No class.

That night the three tables in the VIP Lounge looked like slim pickings. I turned to my One9Five Insider and went, 'One footballer? What gives? You're not losing everyone to Sugar Hut are you, babe?'

'Fuck off. Got a couple of soap blokes in and some racing driver over there, but these girls haven't a clue who he is yet so you can get first dibs. Go on, get involved.'

I laughed them off. The racer was so unbelievably fit I actually gasped, but I reminded myself that I just didn't want to go there again. Don't get me wrong, I've had some good times with sportsmen, but I'd made a vow to avoid that crazy life now I was past twenty-five. I was setting my sights on someone who was successful, a business entrepreneur, someone with a bit of get-up-and-go. I was hungry for a lasting relationship with someone I respected. I do not respect sports guys – I just like the lifestyle. If I could have the lifestyle *and* respect him, then we're talking.

I glanced over to see who the girls were talking to and it wasn't great – the two old boys off *EastEnders*. There was so much despair in Gem's eyes, her eyelashes seemed to be melting. Something was up, so I slid over to her. 'Babe, the end of your lash is dangling,' I whispered in her ear. She reacted like I'd told her she had droopy boobs. Her eyes went all watery, but she held it together.

'Fuck it. Shit. You have to come to the toilets right now,' she said, dragging me off.

As soon as we got in the toilets, Gem started sobbing

big time. 'Calm it, Gem. It's only a fake eyelash,' I said, all confused. The moody toilet attendant didn't even move to pass the tissues, so I click-clacked off to the cubicle to get some loo roll and sat Gem on a toilet seat.

'Oh God, stop crying,' she kept telling herself as she fanned her face. By this point it was too late and she'd gone all puffy and red.

'What's going on? Is it Grant? Has he cheated on you again?'

'It's as bad as that,' she said, letting out a long wail. 'I'm so ugly.' More sobbing. 'My lashes are falling out.'

'What do you mean?' I said, turning her face around with my hand. Looked fine to me.

'I got some lash extensions,' she spluttered. 'And I had a reaction to it. I've only got a quarter of my real lashes left.'

Shit. This *was* serious. 'So where'd you get these lashes from?' I asked.

'I put on some Girls Aloud fake lashes. Everyone says Kimberley's are the best, but look at me. I look like a tramp,' she said, pulling at them. It wasn't the right time to say this, but everyone knows Cheryl's are the best. Since that bombshell would've sent her over the edge, I kept schtum.

'Babe, it's an outrage. Have you gone back to the eyelash technician?'

'Yeah, but she'd never seen this happen before. She offered to put more in, but I didn't want that cack-handed cow coming anywhere near me. What was she even going to attach them to? I can't even sue them cos I signed some form. It's such a fucking mess.'

'Well, first things first. We're going to reaffix those lashes and calm you down,' I said.

I find I am always really practical in an emergency. Thankfully, I always carry eyelash glue in my clutch. I worked on her blotchy face like it was the Sistine Chapel. I wish there was a job fixing up crying girls' make-up because I'd make a killing in the toilets round here.

'People really don't know the dangers of lash extensions, hun,' I said. 'We got to set up a Facebook group to warn other girls.' I don't think I've ever made such an impassioned speech before. 'We've got to do our bit. That salon needs to be named and shamed.' Mind you, I wasn't going to stop getting my lashes done; just not there.

When we got back to the table, Brooke had moved on from the *EastEnders* blokes (it was inevitable) and was hanging off the footballer with the other girls. She'd gone a step further than them and was having a good feel of his abs. Good on her, but honestly, it's such a cliché – these blokes always have an 'understanding' wife back in their palatial homes in Chigwell who put up with their husbands' penchant for doing lines off naked girls in hotel rooms. All I know is that it's preferable being the other woman to being the wife – same perks, no humiliation. These types are always properly suited and booted, but their IQs match the numbers on their shirts. Still, every girl has to try one out; it's an Essex rite of passage.

I can't even be bothered to go into the story of the premiership footballer I was doing a while back because it was so brief and boring. And that was just the sex. The nights out and presents were top-notch, and the parties would be fuelled by lines and lines of Colombian goodness (I don't touch class As any more unless it's a special occasion). He funded some crazy nights out, but the pay-off wasn't worth the misery in the bedroom. I knew something was up when he said, 'You're moving too much, just lie still,' as he continued to pump away. And I did as I was told! I can only guess any movement would have broken his concentration.

Anyway, lying there gave me a lot of time to question the relationship and the allure of footballers generally. My sister claims that in 1995 David Beckham chatted her up at the Castle in Woodford. I suppose he did have bad hair back then and a squeaky voice, which would definitely have put her off. But how different things could have been if she'd become Tasha Beckham. For one thing, I wouldn't still be going down One9Five.

I started to spiral into a depression watching these girls fawn all over the footballer, and then this Italian-looking bloke comes over to me. Let's just call him Gino Ginelli.

'I'd really like to buy you a drink,' he says to me intensely.

I was sobering up, so I thought, what's the harm, even though I didn't fancy him. He was quite old, perhaps forty, and balding, but he had a lot of swagger about him.

'Yeah, go on then, how about a bottle of Grey Goose for me and the girls,' I said, pointing in their direction. A lot of Essex men would make a big deal of that request and say stuff like, 'Gawd, women, they want the earth,' and do that mock moaning thing to flirt. I mean, why ask if you're not going to put your money where your mouth is? But this guy didn't even flinch, waved over the girl waiting his table and got the drinks in. There was something quite unnerving about him so I instinctively felt like I needed to fob him off a bit.

'You know what? My ex keeps looking over. He's a bit jel like that.'

'You still like him?' asked Gino.

'I don't fancy him still, but I wouldn't want to do anything to hurt him either,' I said, giving a pretty measured answer.

'What would he do if he saw you kissing another man?'

'I suppose it'd have to happen sometime, but it's a bit too soon for that.'

'Why, when did you split up from him?' All his

questions were really monosyllabic and a bit cold, if you ask me. I wasn't enjoying this exchange at all.

'Two and a bit years ago, but it's still a bit raw for him.'

'I'd kiss you,' he said suddenly. Even though I hadn't flirted with him one single bit, he'd seen some sort of green light. I swear I've got some sort of sexual beam that just cannot be dimmed. It's the cross I must bear as a Gemini.

'Oh, right, that's nice of you,' was all I could think to say back.

'No, you don't understand. I would kiss you. Right now.'

'Oh, lovely.' My breathing was starting to get shallow, which is not good because I usually keel over if that carries on too long. 'Yay, the vodka's here!' I screamed manically. He didn't even look away from me. I'm telling you, he made me feel proper nervous.

I urgently signalled the girls over to diffuse the tension some more. Gino got the bar guy mixing our various drink requests, and I double-checked Gem's lashes weren't wilting again. She winked at me as if to say, 'Get in there, girl,' but I shook my head with wide eyes and whispered to her, 'He's not the full ticket, hun. Proper issues.' To be honest, I was slightly insulted she'd think I'd want to try it on with a balding Italian. Seriously, not impressed.

I was a bit scared he'd stick around after he'd bought

all that booze, but he just went off back to his table. Everything seemed to right itself, so me and the girls turned to the dance floor to assess the talent. I'd seen better days. The floor is actually lit up, but it's proper small and the bouncers have a go at you if you dance with a drink in your hand. You can't even walk across it if you're clutching a glass. Since I don't like to leave my drink behind, there'd have to be a pretty amazing bloke to get me dancing out there. Fortunately there wasn't, but that was fine because I was quite content sipping my Moscow Mule.

Just as I was applying more lip gloss and feeling pretty der-runk (lip gloss maintenance needs to be done every twenty minutes however wasted you are), my buzz was instantly killed by some staggering skank of a girl. If I was the suspicious type, I'd swear she done it on purpose. Tia Maria and orange all down my back. All I could think of spluttering was, 'What the fuck?'

'Don't cry about it, darling,' this bitch laughed back. The red mist descended and it was just instinct to chuck the dregs of my Mule in her face. What a waste, but worth it. She flipped and started going, 'Don't you know who I am? I'm Johnny Fawkes's daughter.'

I have no idea who this is. When I do find out, no doubt it will be with Johnny Fawkes's gun against my head.

Charlie turned to me and went, 'Do you want her removed,' so obviously I didn't spare her. He dragged her off kicking and screaming as her tragic mates followed. Buh-bye, ladies. Hate to say it, but it is pretty satisfying to wield a smidgeon of power. I've worked hard to make my mark socially, and that is just one of the pay-offs.

After that, I tried to enjoy myself but I so wasn't feeling it. We'd had a laugh, we'd drunk the drink, and my heels were giving me grief. I got talking to Jade Goody at Nu Bar once and she told me she'd soak her feet in vodka before going out so her feet never felt a thing. God rest her soul, but really?

Just as I was getting the girls to finish up their drinks, that Gino bloke comes back over.

'My friend over there likes you,' he said, pointing at the racing driver.

'Good for him,' I replied dismissively. I'd honestly had enough of this weirdo.

'He asked me if I thought you like to have a good time, so I came over to check. And you do. So here's the good news. He's asked me to ask you to come back to ours for an after-party. What you say?' asked Gino.

I was proper gobsmacked. What the hell was going on? Was it this Gino's job to herd up girls for the Jenson Button of Essex? How insulting . . . how cheap . . . how exciting.

I'd heard of this happening before. Years back, Cleo went to see this Essex comedian who's a fucking big deal now. She was sat in the front row, and during the interval a man came up to a few brunettes in the audience, including Cleo, and said the comedian had requested their company backstage afterwards. Mr Comedy was actually picking out girls during his act and giving his personal shopper the list as soon as he walked off stage. I thought it sounded humiliating at the time, but then it did make Cleo's year. It was pretty grubby what those two got up to, and she was at his beck and call for months.

So the way I saw it, I could either go back home and carry on with life, or I could take a risk and see what hanging out with a racing driver was like. I'd never done one of them before. After my sister's David Beckham non-incident, she did end up dating a guy who played for West Ham in the late Nineties. That's actually not one of her tall stories cos I saw the romance unfold with my very own eyes. Back then, everyone called him Fatty, so he really wasn't a catch. He used to go down the Horse & Well in Woodford with his West Ham mates and have legendary nights of debauchery. Fatty's a big star now, but scandalous pictures used to get circulated when the old landlord got pissed.

It was while Fatty was standing on the pool table with his trousers round his ankles that he first laid eyes on my sister. It's the stuff of true romance. He was loud and lairy, but he did treat my sister like a princess most of the time, and she still feeds off stories about where he took her and what he gave her. (Genital herpes.) (Not really, it was just cystitis, but I like winding her up.) I suppose when you've got a kid and you're married to the irritant that is Tony Crook, you cling to the days when famous blokes were sniffing around.

I know I had made a vow to quit all that mucking around, but I'm full of it really. It's not like I had any better offers. It might be the most epic error of judgement, but then again, every Essex girl loves a drama and I truly believe in following your urges.

Oh, and I didn't follow all the other girls back to his, if that's what you're thinking. Bit classier than that, aren't I? Brooke made a booty call to the fit bloke she'd met in Nu Bar that night, but that's totally different. That had been her agenda that night. I'm sure the racing driver got his end away with a few of those girls, but I wanted to set myself apart.

Here's the thing. You don't go back to his if you want to see him again. As my nan says, 'Nobody's going to buy the cow if they can get the milk for free.' She's seen a few things, so she's knows what she's talking about. And let's face it, men like the excitement of the chase. It's how they were hardwired as cavemen, and there's not been much progress since. So the rule is, have at least one date before you put out.

I thought about Gino's proposition and I decided I needed to go over to the racing driver to let him know what he wouldn't be getting that night. He was sat down with two girls either side of him who were laughing like maniacs. I hate girls who use fake laughter as their flirting weapon. So lame. He seemed to be enjoying himself, as any man would if his ego was being fanned, but as I got close he shot me a look and then didn't take his eyes off me as these girls continued fawning all over him. I suddenly got all tongue-tied. I can't do him justice in words, but he looked like a tanned Freddie Ljungberg with stubble. And these amazing green eyes. I just stood there like a lemming and it took him to get up and come over to me in the end. That so wasn't the plan, but at least he'd left those two silly girls behind. I could see they were mad as hell, but I couldn't help that.

'I was hoping you'd come over,' were his first words. I was still struck dumb. 'I'm Ben and you are . . .' Thankfully I snapped out of it and rebooted my mouth.

'Becci. Umm, I was just wondering what sort of person invites lots of women back to his place for a party?'

'I would say a person that has a good eye for good women,' he replied.

'Well, hun, I'd have to agree with you there, but honestly, it's a bit weird, right? And your mate's a bit full-on too. I wouldn't bother getting him to do your dirty work in the future.'

'Babe, I take your point and I promise to do all my own dirty work from now on,' he replied, winking. 'So you going to join us or what?'

'I don't think so. I'm not really into orgies,' I said.

'Who said anything about orgies, babe? It's a group of people drinking and partying.'

He spent the next ten minutes spinning the usual lines like how fit I was, how all the blokes were looking at him all jel because I was talking to him, and he even said he'd tell all the other girls to do one because I was the one he wanted. And so on. Now if I'd been an amateur, I would've been feeling like the most special girl in the room right then. The whole time we were talking, I honestly felt like he only had eyes for me, but you can't be under any illusion. The West Essex player is a seasoned pro and you're just listening to his set repertoire. And I'll admit, it feels good to believe it at the time, but if you turn them down they will have five other girls on speed-dial, all of them thinking they're equally special. I don't think this guy even needed speed-dial when there was no shortage of takers in this club. I was clearly playing with fire here, but I was determined to play him right back.

I had my work cut out, though. He nearly drew me in a couple of times, but I managed to negotiate my way out. And believe me, he wasn't easy to resist. Especially when I found out he'd met Fernando Alonso several times on the racing scene. I'm not fucking kidding you. That was the moment I caved in and gave him my phone number. So cunning. The more he talked about his life, the more I envisioned stays in Dubai in those incredible hotels, us by the swimming pool and us bumping into Fernando Alonso, his brows all thick and that sexy Spanish accent. Sometimes I play out scenarios in my head so well that I'm convinced that's the way it's going to pan out. Anyways, before you write me off as a complete delusional wannabe, let me tell you that my game plan paid off. Just five minutes after I'd walked out the club, he called me.

When you hear from them in the taxi home, you've just secured yourself a date.

3

Family comes First

I was majorly hanging at Gemma's the next day. Such an epic error mixing champagne with vodka. That's just asking for it. I drove home at old-lady-speed and slept it off for another couple of hours. But there's only one solution when I'm feeling this delicate, so I pulled on my Ugg boots and made my way over to Jackie and Don's. Those ten metres on gravel are hard work when you're all broken.

'Bacon sarnie and tea?' said Mum way too loudly. I was too weak to manage more than a nod before resting my face on the black marble breakfast table. Marilyn came running up to my chair but I had nothing to give. Marilyn's my blonde Pomeranian and Mum looks after him while I'm at work and when I'm out. He's not good at spending time in his own company.

Oh yeah, so my boy dog has a girl's name – *somebody*

62

(Don Fox) got mugged off. We were going to breed her, but by the time we realized Marilyn had a dick, I was too attached to him. Although I do think he's a gay, as before he had the snip, he'd always hump Jake's leg. My brother's scent attracts a lot of dogs.

'Don't forget Cheryl and Sue are coming over for Sunday lunch,' trilled Mum. I let out a despairing groan and looked up to make sure she was getting on with the bacon. She wasn't. My tear ducts were so dried up from dehydration, all I could do was cry on the inside. Too preoccupied with her bloody First Wives Club to think of the needs of her sick child.

Cheryl and Sue have been divorced since their mid-forties and Mum lives vicariously through them. I don't know why because Mum gets checked out ten times more than they do. Or maybe people think she's Jo Wood. Honestly, the resemblance is uncanny. And they all go out on the pull, which is just gross. Well, Mum claims she isn't pulling, but she sees herself as this wise relationship guru. This is one conversation I heard them have once:

SUE: 'I got this text from a mystery number. So I
    thought it's either Neil or that tennis player.'
CHERYL: 'Oh yeah, that tennis player was fit.'
SUE: 'So I texted back and I've not heard a word
    since.'
MUM: 'Right, next time we're in the Vault, you send

him a text saying, "We're out, let me know if you're about too."'

SUE: 'Yeah, I will do. But to be honest, I'm too busy, what with the business and the kids, so I don't know when I could fit in a date.'

Doesn't that sound like a conversation you have when you're fourteen? Except the bit about the business and the kids. Seriously, though, at their age, why are they so confused about men? She couldn't understand why the tennis player bothered to text her in the first place. Because, Sue, he is texting lots of other women. Plus I bet he's just a tennis coach down David Lloyd club.

I sometimes think I should teach a class at Epping Forest College on how to play the players. Mum's an old romantic so never bought my theory on this tennis player, but then I've grown up using texting as a dating weapon. They're all naïve to think this guy's been waiting years to meet a woman like Sue and this text is the start of the most amazing relationship. People hide behind texts. It's like dipping a toe in the dating water but you don't have to commit. Eurggh – imagine in the olden days when the only option was calling their home phone? You'd have no time to think up your excuse if you were on the receiving end. I can't say no to blokes if they ask for my number, but at least I can ignore the text when it comes. But you got to love Sue's storytelling, which in the end makes out that *she's* the one who hasn't got time for the tennis player. A classic switcheroo.

It's quite disturbing, the amount of cougars out on the prowl in West Essex, but they stick to their places so I rarely have to see it unless Mum insists we start the night off together for some mother–daughter bonding. I'm always pretty proud to be seen out with her because, like I say, she is a serious stunner. Blonde, a tiny figure, good legs, and she does have this rock chic thing about her, but maybe that's just her love of cropped leather jackets. Hate to use this word, but she's a total MILF. Back in the Seventies, Don and Jackie were a seriously hot couple. While she looked like the wife of a Rolling Stone, my dad was the spit of Harrison Ford, so that's how he bagged a classy bird like Mum. Unfortunately, Dad doesn't look like Harrison any more, but he does have a lovely head of salt 'n' pepper hair on him and he's in really good shape. He's on that rowing machine of his almost every day. I honestly think they're motivated by wanting to look good for each other, which is pretty sweet after thirty-two years of marriage. As long as Mum still thinks he's the most handsome man in Buckhurst Hill, that's all that matters.

The Vault Champagne and Wine Bar in Woodford is a favourite haunt of the First Wives Club and it's as creepy as it sounds. I mean, imagine you're sat there enjoying a cold glass of fizz and you clock this woman who's got her back to you – an amazing body, all toned, hot black dress, thick glossy hair. She turns around and it's a whole different story. Body like *Baywatch*, face like *Crimewatch*. It would be nice if the doorman stopped any disturbed-looking people as they left the Vault to say, 'Please don't have nightmares.' Honestly, images of Sue grinding up against various white-haired gangster types will be with me for life.

With shaky hands I managed to pour myself an orange juice, then gave Mum what for on the bacon and tea front. She said something about not being a mind-reader. I would have thought it was obvious that it was a yes to the food and drink, looking at the state of me.

While I was waiting for breakfast, I managed to climb the stairs to find Jake. No surprises, he was sat there in his pants playing Grand Auto Theft or whatever it is. I swear that game's made him more disrespectful towards me, what with all that running over of women.

'Alright, Jacob?' He nodded in my direction, which meant I was allowed into his bedroom. I didn't go all the way in since the room was ripe with an aroma of sweat and tramp wee. I honestly don't know how he does it. It does my head in because all my mates are completely charmed by Jake. I'll admit, he's a good-looking boy if you like the Matt Damon type. I just wish they could see the golden boy in all his glory.

'What you get up to last night?'

'Football club dinner and Sugar Hut,' he went.

'Oh yeah? See anyone interesting?'

'Pretty much the whole lot from *TOWIE*. And that nutcase Sascha.'

Sascha's this girl he'd been trying to shake off. Or as he put it, he was 'winding down the relationship'. I can relate to that. You've got to do stuff in stages, otherwise it's a bit of a shock. Sascha is a complete psycho when it comes to blokes. We actually call her 'Legs' to her face, which she takes as a compliment, but it's because she's guaranteed to leg it out of a bar so her boyfriend chases after her. How controlling is that? I was well surprised when Jake started seeing her. He hasn't got very high tolerance levels, and the first time she did a runner, he just shrugged his shoulders and turned back to the bar. I mean, it's a risky game for her to play because once you've run out, then what? Go home. Only person you've hurt is yourself, Sascha. Luckily she's now found some mug who actually plays along and seems to enjoy the chase. It's reassuring to know there's someone for everyone, however unstable you are.

A girlfriend isn't high up on Jake's agenda. I would say this is his list of priorities from top to bottom: his mates, football, sex, swindling innocents, his clothes, white-collar boxing, family. Yeah, we're definitely at the bottom. He doesn't swindle much, but he's always got some money-making project under way. He went to Thailand on his gap year (not that he went to university, so that's a gap from Essex), met some Thai business guys and comes back claiming he's going to import

Chinese lanterns. Well, my baby bro was spot-on – they literally took off the moment he brought them back here. If you see one floating in the sky at a wedding, just remember that's Jake Fox's doing.

He's also a carpet fitter in one of Dad's businesses, so eventually he'll have to choose between his dodgy Thai deals and running the carpet shop. His motto is 'Do something dangerous every day'. Sometimes that really works out for him, and sometimes it doesn't. He could have been fleeced by those Thai lantern blokes, but the risk paid off. But then he once decided to ride his BMX at high speed under a road barrier and ended up skinning his entire back. That risk didn't pay off. But Jake says if his head had been an inch higher he'd have knocked his block off, so he was lucky. That's a major understatement.

'So what time did you get home?'

'About six a.m.'

'What? So where'd you go after Sugar Hut?'

'Back to Mick's gaff. Drank some more and stuff.'

I really wasn't getting much out of him but I had no interest in finding out what he'd been up to there. Since Mick Norcross got notoriety through *TOWIE*, I'm always hearing about after-parties going on at his. That family know how to have a good time and Mick's got to be the most eligible granddad in Essex. If it's not Mick people are drinking with, it's Kirk or his brother Dan. I swear every bloke round here knows a Norcross.

Downstairs I could hear some sort of kerfuffle which I thought was either my bacon or Mum's mutton (that's Cheryl and Sue to you). I walked downstairs slowly and peered into the kitchen. Guess who the fuck was there? Only the bloody racing driver! I still don't know how he found out where I lived. I keep forgetting to ask people for this vital information, but I reckon it must have been my insider down One9Five. And there he was, talking to my mum in the kitchen with Cheryl and Sue. If I'd had more strength I would have slapped myself to make sure I wasn't dreaming. I staggered back upstairs to Jake.

'Do me a favour, Jake?' He didn't even look up from his game. 'Jake. Look at me. Jake. Stop playing . . . *Jayyyyyyyyke*,' I screeched, snatching the console from his hands. Now he was looking at me, but he looked like he was about to hit me. Hard to believe it, but I actually used to beat him in fights. These days I find myself in a lot of headlocks so I try to avoid all confrontations with him if possible.

'What the fuck are you playing at? Give us that,' he said, getting up.

'Chill your boots, I've put it on pause. Listen, this is important. There's a bloke down in the kitchen talking to Mum. Go downstairs and if they ask if I'm about, tell them I drove over to Brooke's.'

'That's a shit lie for starters cos your Audi's in the drive.'

'Oh yeah, good point. Alright, tell them I'm asleep up here then and I'm really unwell.'

'Fine, but you owe me. Who's this geezer anyway?'

'Never you mind. And can you bring up the bacon sandwich while you're down there?'

He was gone for a good ten minutes. I started to fret so much that I didn't realize I had sat down on Jake's skanky sheets. Urggh. Boys and black sheets are such a bad combo. Eventually he came back with a half-eaten bacon sandwich. Majorly gutted.

'What's your problem with Ben? He's well sound.' I'd actually forgotten the racing driver's name up until that point.

'My problem is that I don't like people dropping over unannounced and he's a stalker. Did you tell them I was sick?'

'Sick in the head? Yes I did, you silly cow.' Charming.

'And what'd he say?'

'He said he'd come by another time.'

'Oh good, and then he went?'

'No, he's still down there with Mum, Cheryl and Sue. I think he's staying over for the roast.'

'You fucking what?' I spluttered. I sneaked downstairs to check. He was still there and the 'ladies' were all over him like a rash. They were sabotaging my chances! Then I saw Dad walk into the kitchen. That was game over as far as I was concerned.

I went back upstairs and lay on Mum and Dad's bed to work out my next move. That's when I heard a car revving up. I went over to the window and it was Ben leaving in a red Mercedes. I'm not sure if he saw me, but I fell to the floor quickly. I've never been so relieved. I crawled out the room so I couldn't be seen and then went over to Jake's room.

'You fucking wind-up merchant.'

'Just given you a taste of your own piss-take medicine.'

It was a fair point.

Although I had a lot to thank him for, as all that adrenalin totally shifted the hangover. I really appreciated my day after that lucky escape, but I stayed clear of the house because everyone kept grilling me about Ben. And I had no answers. This was a total first for me, so I didn't really know what to do next. I didn't have his number, so I was just waiting for a text to find out why the hell he'd come over. Except I was just left hanging because I didn't hear a thing from him.

I'm sorry, but that just annoys me.

4

Start calling the Shots

The next fews days passed without any drama. I went to the wholesalers, I got Gem to agree to us all wearing coral and we went to Russ and Rob's birthday night at Luxe. The club had just reopened after a complete facelift – same owner, new name. The place was damaged goods after becoming a scene for major fights. When I say major, I mean a hundred and fifty people really going for it on Loughton High Street, and before that a twenty-person knife fight. Even when it comes to brawling, people round here can't stand not being a part of the action.

But I got to say, I've been warming to Luxe since Nu Bar gets all the *TOWIE* tourists on Saturdays now. It's just too small for that, whereas Luxe has gone more upmarket and the kids are kept out. Russ had hired out the whole place, and on the invite he'd promised 'a red-carpet entrance, celebrities and dancing fire-eaters'.

Like I said, he'd been in the background in three scenes of *TOWIE* and at this time he was making out he was friend to the stars. Barry the Bouncer was the most famous person to walk up Russ' red carpet and that's only cos he went over to chat with one of his mates on the door. His 'best friend' Kirk didn't show up, but it turned out to be a top night anyway. To give him credit, he did have an amazing turnout and he had hired two fire-eaters. They each weighed twenty stone and, unfortunately, they did dance.

There was one dramatic change in my life, though. I took my Audi TT in for an MOT and came out the garage with a Mercedes SLR. Don't ask me how that happened. I was trying to budget at the time too, but this car just had a bit more swag about it. I mean, I traded it in, plus it's a vintage car now they've stopped making them, so essentially it's an investment piece. Goes without saying, I bought it on finance. Dad's allowance and my earnings don't make me a millionaire, you know! And before you start, if you had Don and Jackie Fox for parents, you'd charge too. It was a pretty good few days as I did a lot of cruising with Brooke in the SLR when she was on standby. I recall we spent a lot of time down Virgin Active, talking in the pool, chilling in the sauna and getting treatments at Harmony. Before you get jel and start accusing me of being a slacker, I was doing wedding fairs at the weekends so I could chill here and there during the week. Tasha would disagree, but I'm sort of my own boss.

Driving back from one of these hectic days, I got a call from Tasha. I had finally worked out how to plug my iPhone into the car, so I took my first call on the car speaker. Pretty flash, right?

'Becci, where are you?'

'Just coming back to the shop, but I've got to drop Brooke off first.'

'Well, there's a bloke here says he knows you. Ben? Yeah, he's called Ben.' Then she whispered something which I think was 'He's fit.' Unless I heard what I wanted to hear. She could have said, 'You shit.' The thing is, I was too stunned to even talk or listen.

'Shut up!' squealed Brooke, followed by, 'Fuck, you just ran a red light . . . No, don't stop. Keep driving, hun.'

I was all confused. I had to pull over.

'Tasha, I'm coming straight back. Be there in ten,' I said and hung up. What the fuck was this Ben playing at? Now he knew where I worked. Mum must have said something.

'OMG, Becs, what you going to do? Hide again?'

'No, babe, I'm nipping this stalker in the bud. I'm going to confront him. Woman to man. I mean, what if he starts showing up at every club, every beauty salon, the doggy day spa, going through my bins. It's getting out of control.'

'I love it when you do fighting talk,' said Brooke with genuine admiration in her voice.

'How's my hair and make-up?' I asked.

'You've never looked better.' So true. We had just come from getting our eyelashes done. How lucky was that?

I didn't have time to drop Brooke off, so she had to come to the shop too. I think she would have missed a flight to watch this palaver play out anyway. I burst in looking all determined with Brooke in my wake. And then I saw him. And he was flirting with my sister.

Well, new tactics were called for altogether. I know she's married and five years older than me, but that means nothing when it comes to sisterly rivalry. So I turned on the charm and then some.

'Hun, I can't believe you're in my shop,' I said, bouncing towards him.

'My shop,' butted in Tasha. So I jutted out the baps. It is moments like this that I am one hundred per cent glad I bought them. Actually, Nan got them for me. Was it for my nineteenth? She's paid for all of her granddaughters to have some sort of surgery, so don't go thinking I get special treatment. Tasha got her lips pumped up and a tummy tuck, thank God. But that would be no help to her now. I could see Ben was transfixed by the 34Ds.

'Alright, sweet cheeks?' were his first words to me. I'll never forget that moment. I think I might get it tattooed on my inner thigh, I love it that much. It was a proper thunderbolt moment. He was even hotter than I remembered. I'm sorry, but who's not a sucker for a tanned, toned man? He was wearing a white V-neck T-shirt under a black jacket and jeans. I caught a flash of a gold Cartier watch on his wrist too. My eyesight is *very* good.

'Yeah, fine thanks. You been looking for me?'

'You're a hard lady to pin down. You feeling better now?'

'What?'

'You was ill when I came over to your parents'.'

'Oh yeah, just had the lurgy. I was a bit weak for visitors.'

'So nothing to do with your mate Grey Goose?'

'Nah, can't blame her. I think it was just the vodka.'

'That's what I meant.' Shit, I was being such a lemon. Grey Goose is what we call Brooke because she's convinced she's going grey. Why would he be referring to that? Basically, my Essex brain takes my normal brain hostage in moments of panic. It's a major affliction and there is no cure.

'Yeah, I knew you meant that. I was just joking,' I said, turning to Brooke. Her head was down and her shoulders were shaking. What a bitch. Move it on, my normal brain screamed. 'So what can I do for you, anyway?'

'I just wanted to take you out for dinner and drinks if you fancied it.'

'You could have just texted me that. No need talk to my parents and my sister. A bit extreme, don't you reckon?' That question was slightly pass-agg (that's passive-aggressive to you. I'm well big on the pass-agg).

'Texting's not my style, hun,' he said, flashing me the whitest smile. 'Texting's for boys. Nicer to arrange a date in person, don't you think?'

'Oh yeah, it's just unusual, that's all.' I was melting on the inside. I'd only known him for about thirty-five minutes of my life, but he'd turned what I thought I knew about men upside down. Yeah, he was liking the chase, but this was well extreme.

'How you fixed for tonight?'

'I'm totally free.' Stupid Essex brain was piping up again. I'm only repeating my blunders so you know what not to do. I sounded as keen as Marilyn when he spots a leg to hump. Before I had time to style it out, he was already making arrangements.

'Right, I'll pick you up at eight p.m. tonight and get us a table at Sheesh.' I had to contain my excitement because I'd been dying to go there for ages. I mean, get this – I tried to book a table there for Mother's Day in March, and they told me there was no space at weekends until August *and* I'd have to put down a deposit! Then they asked in all sincerity whether I wanted to book a table for then. What a joke. I phoned up the Ivy and it turns out I could have got a table there if I'd wanted it. I didn't, I just wanted to prove a point about how out of control things can get around here. The hype is all down to it being owned by Alan Sugar. To be clear, he says he's just the landlord and has no part in it, but he promotes it enough. So I had been thinking, screw you, Sheesh, I don't want to go there anyway, but a girl's allowed to change her tune.

'Lovely, eight it is. Obviously you know where I live.' I meant that to come out as pass-agg again, but it ended up being a merry trill instead.

You may have twigged already, but by this point I had decided not to take out a restraining order on Ben. I did want to get one on myself, though. I am always the cool one and I wasn't about to let this man turn all that around. I thought all this as his tight butt walked its way out the shop and popped itself in the Mercedes. My sister turned to me and went, 'You jammy bitch.'

'Watch and learn, Tash,' I replied as smugly as possible. She always bleats on about how blessed she is to have a husband and a kid, so I'm forced to look for any opportunity to throw it back in her face. Petty, I know. We're actually polar opposites. She's got a slick black bob, she's tall, never wears heels and was always desperate to settle down. Whereas I got big blonde hair, I'm petite, never seen out of heels and desperate to stay out. I swear we got different dads.

Brooke and I went to celebrate the only way we knew how: dancing in the stock room to Hed Kandi while wearing two new wedding dresses. I can't be the only bridal boutiquer to do this, right? Tasha stopped the fun though because she was jel and we had to do a fitting. Like I really had time for that with less than five hours to get ready!

I don't know how I did it but I did. Brooke came back with me and we managed to do an emergency spray in my tanning tent. Dad bought it after I kept tanning the carpet. You just forget, don't you, when you're spraying yourself that the mist gets everything? And then you end up with these two perfect footmarks in the white carpet. Dad was livid by the time he bought the third carpet, even though I pointed out how lucky he was to own a carpet shop and have a carpet fitter for a son. Not impressed. He was so happy when his mate told him about tan tents. I can totally let loose with the spray now (I swear only to ever use St Tropez or Lancôme Flash Bronzer if I'm forced to home-tan). I know I said I'm against on-the-day tans, but I was really pale because I'd planned on having a quiet one that weekend. I can always find an excuse to bend the rules.

Then I had to do my make-up, create massive hair *and* choose an outfit. We were well pleased with ourselves. Brooke said she'd totally do me if she were a bloke. Let me talk you through my look: a short cream dress with gold sequins, and I put a sparkly black silk jacket over the top with rolled-up sleeves. Then I went for a quilted pink Chanel bag with nude peep-toe heels. And we did my hair in a messy up-do – thank God

I'd got those extensions otherwise I'd have been a major flathead. I made Victoria Beckham look scruffy that night. For once in my life, I was ready ahead of time.

Brooke had gone home in a taxi, so I decided to chill out in the kitchen with Marilyn to pass the time. I picked up his Jimmy Chew and he growled at me. So cute! It's this squishy toy in the shape of a stiletto and he won't go anywhere without it now. He's so my dog. I threw it across the kitchen and Marilyn went skidding after it and straight into Dad's feet.

'Hello, Honkytonks,' he said. He always calls me this when I'm dressed up smart, and I just know he's mocking me as he knows no better. 'You look like you're going to be sick, Princess. Tell yer old man what's up?'

'Nothing's wrong, I've just got a date,' I snapped.

'Hmmm, interesting. Not like my little girl to look so anxious. You got frown lines going on and everything.' See, even Dad could tell I wasn't the cool one any more. *And* I was ageing before him. Not good. 'Is it that Ben bloke?'

'Yeah, it is, if you must know.'

'Hmmm, *very* interesting. Nice bloke, that. I reckon he could have his pick of the bunch, but he chose you, love, so what's to worry about?'

'I'm not worried. I just don't know him very well so I'm a bit nervous.'

'Oh, I've talked to him loads. What you want to know?'

This was a turn-up for the books. I'm normally quite secretive when it comes to blokes I'm seeing, so I felt well uncomfortable that Dad had chatted him up before me.

'Don't trouble yourself, Dad. I know you're mates and all, but I think I'll just find out for myself.'

'Suit yourself, girl. But I just want you to know that I want him for my son-in-law. He can get us into the Monaco Grand Prix for free. So no pressure or nothing.'

If you want to relax before a big event, don't go to Don Fox. I felt sick. The truth is, I actually think Dad's a really good judge of character and he seemed to be besotted with Ben already. He'd just raised the stakes for me.

There was a beep outside. I felt like changing, I was so hot. I suppose I could have taken my jacket off, but that would have ruined the look.

'Why do people always hoot? Why can't people get out the car and ring the doorbell anymore?' Ha, I knew Dad couldn't stay sweet on Ben for long. He loves a good moan.

'Bye, Dad. Do not stay up.' Even though I live across the way, he doesn't go to bed until the light over my front door is off. And the sitting room is dead opposite mine, so he'll just sit there in his leather armchair, legs up, a tumbler of Glenfiddich in hand, glaring at the TV, but he's really looking through the French windows at my front door. It's all a bit Tony Soprano, if I'm to be honest. Not that he's dedicated, because I've never seen him awake in that chair once.

I tottered over to the car (have I mentioned my shoes yet? Louboutins. Say no more) and he leant over the passenger seat to open the door. Now, I'm quite tiny, but this car was so low I was practically sitting on the floor. I spent most of the drive to Chigwell thinking about how I was going to exit without crawling out or being yanked up. It's at times like these that I'm glad I'm a girl who wears knickers. If I'm ever famous, no pap will ever get an up-skirt shot of me thanks to Nan. Back in the day, she used to drop us off at Faces or Charlie Chan's in her black Mini. I was always like, 'Nan, whatever you do, do not drop us off right outside the door.' Every time she did and it was impossible not to flash some pant as we clambered out the back. It's hard to believe that was a decade ago, and now look at me in a red Mercedes, I thought. I took a sideward glance at Ben, this stunning man driving this stunning car, and then I checked my own face in the overhead-mirror. Yeah, it was definitely me. I looked composed but my mouth was twitching, dying to betray the high-pitched screams going on in my head. I'd only gone and bagged myself a proper winner. What a moment.

Just as I was starting to feel a bit emotional with my meteoric rise, we rocked up at Sheesh's gates in record time. He wasn't all talk – he really could drive fast. In the end he just walked round to my door and pulled me out without asking. Smooth.

'So how did you get a table here on a Friday night anyway?' I said, finally breaking the silence.

'Know Dylan, don't I?' he replied.

If you're smart in West Essex, you should get to know the owner of every elite establishment. I made a mental note of the name cos there was no way I was going on a four-month waiting list again.

Just the outside of the restaurant was pure glamour. There were flaming torches at the entrance, a couple of huge metal statues and Ben's Mercedes looked the business in a car park full of Lambos and Ferraris. When we walked in, there was the usual Essex-bloke greeting. A lot of shouting, followed by a lot of hugs where they pull each other in violently and smack each other's backs, and a lot of mate this and mate that. One thing they never do, though, is tousle each other's hair. It's majorly disrespectful. I've seen fights break out if that line has been crossed.

Despite my initial anger towards Sheesh, I was totally blown away. It used to be a well ancient pub called the King's Head, but what old man Shugs had done was pretty special. I'm doubting Alan chose the classy colour scheme, but it oozes 'man', if you know what I mean. Dark wood, cowhide furniture, imprinted leather chairs, dark booths, gilded mirrors, open fires, a cigar cabinet. And in the corner of the bar, there was one thing that makes an Essex establishment a real winner: a piano. I don't know what it is about a piano, but round here we can't get enough of it. If it's a joint where you can actually get *on* the piano, then the bar will be packed. It's a simple secret to Essex success. That's why we love a crooner like Arg – a crooner comes with a piano. There must be some deep psychological meaning to all this, but I can't work it out. And the final ingredient in an Essex restaurant is noise. We like a bit of a din going on because then it feels like we're all having a good time. And obviously everyone in the restaurant looked the nuts. Dressing up's not just for clubs and bars, you know.

We got shown to our table, which was very cosy. We were in the Leather Lounge, but I had a quick nose around the place and it was all lush. They even had a Love Lounge, but it's pretty intimate and you'd have to be in there with other couples. I'd be earwigging the whole time, so I was pretty glad he hadn't booked us a table in there. In these plush surroundings, I've got to say he looked even better looking. Dark wood must make green eyes stand out or something because I was transfixed. I honestly felt like the luckiest girl in the room, but I had to remind myself that this was just a bit of fun. Even the waitress was openly flirting with him, but he didn't bite. He did everything right. He was really relaxed, smiley, attentive, and I was a bit confused, to be honest, because he didn't seem like the same cocksure bloke I'd met before.

When I first saw him in One9Five, I think I was put off by girls salivating all over him. I don't do dribbling. But take him out of that setting and here was a better-looking, more genuine bloke. I wasn't going to pretend that I'd forgotten all about his indecent proposal from the club, though. I'm no mug. So I lulled him into a false sense of security. I let him order a bottle of Cristal and explain what the Turkish grub options were and then I went in for the kill.

'So I was just wondering, did you have that party in the end?'

He laughed, which wasn't the response I'd been after.

'It's not a crime to enjoy the company of girls, is it?' he said. 'I only invited you because I thought you were a bit of a sort and you might have had fun there. And before you ask, that guy wasn't a pimp, he's my manager. We both got taste is all. I don't know why you're all suspicious. People have parties. And girls go to them.'

'I'm surprised I'm even out with you, to be honest,' I said. He didn't even look offended.

'Well, I'm glad you are, because I'd have been in bits if I'd been denied the pleasure of your face one more time,' he said. 'You've got something about you, Becs, and I can't quite put my finger on it yet.' There he went with the sweet-talking again, and if he thought I was going to let my guard down after that, he had another thing coming.

'I'm flattered, but you should know this: I'm not like

the other girls round here,' I said, leaning into the table. 'I'm not needy and I have never put up with blokes that mess me about. Yes, I like to be taken out nice places and bought expensive presents, otherwise I won't feel appreciated, but know this. I am my own person and my career goal is not to marry a rich man or become famous. I am an independent woman and you can take it or leave it, hun.'

I took a breath and awaited a reaction. He was seriously frowning and I suddenly felt really nervous. I genuinely thought I'd blown it, which would have been a first.

'That's all very nice, babe, but your menu's on fire.'

He wasn't wrong. Why do waiters leave fucking candles on a table? I panicked and just started banging out the flames with my beautiful Chanel bag. Everyone including my date was pointing and laughing.

How can anyone pick themselves up from this, I hear you ask? Let me share something very special with you. This will shock you, but at Essex Hogwarts I got an A level in Classics. And I've watched a lot of Gerard Butler films. Yep, ask me anything about Aphrodite – the original fun-time Essex girl. She rocked the one-shouldered white dresses long before Essex came along. I think she cheated on her simpleton husband with Adonis (who wouldn't?) but her big love was Greek bad boy Ares. I can't even list how many times she got up the duff. I think she got up the duff with Achilles, didn't she? Anyways, what I learnt was that the gods seriously fuck with humans like they're playthings. Sometimes old Hermes would sink ships just because he was bored. Major dickhead. If you picture these arseholes mugging you off, you can overcome any situation, however brutal it gets. So at school, Gem and I decided we'd make these gods our own and renamed them BHQ – that's Bastards Headquarters to you. So when menus are set on fire or I fall off my wedges and twist my ankle, we just say, 'Up your bum, BHQ,' and totally own it. Never let BHQ see you're upset or they've won.

With my charred Chanel in one hand and my dignity on the floor, I knew what I had to do. Laugh harder. Everyone says I should go into acting and this moment totally proved it. Everyone was now laughing *with* me. Yeah, fuck you all.

'You're a right laugh, Becs,' Ben said, still laughing. I wiped a tear from my eye and hugged my splitting sides with more vigour. Then I held up my menu and bag to show the whole restaurant the remnants. Yeah, I *am* a sport.

'You gotta laugh or you'll cry, right?' I said, regaining some composure.

'I think we're going to get on just fine, babe,' he replied, and looked so deep into my eyes I felt like he was reading my mind. All I could think to say back was, 'Can we get some lamb shish in now?'

Thankfully, my blunder was immediately forgotten when all eyes turned to a birthday girl who was complaining about cold food. They were arguing with this

Martina Cole-type woman and basically her attitude was either eat it or fuck off. Just a word to any *TOWIE* tourists thinking of going here – a lot of our establishments have the West End gloss with the East End attitude. Don't get lulled into a false sense of security as it can kick off at any moment. Imagine you're enjoying yourself in the Ritz but Grant and Phil Mitchell are your waiters. That's the kind of danger I'm talking about. Lovely entertainment if you're watching the drama, though.

I was a bit uptight after my incident and then I felt consumed by fear that I'd have to complain about my food. I couldn't relax until the first course arrived, but it all turned out to be amazing. I was practically having food orgasms at the table. That's when I realized I'd drunk way too much. Epic error. So I don't know if Ben was funny or everything was funny, but we laughed a lot and I felt so hot for him every time he talked about cars. It's like porn to me.

'So what's the deal with the driving? Are you Alonso level or what?' Since I didn't really know the sport I was finding it hard to establish whether he was semi-pro or pro.

'It's going that way,' he said pretty casually. 'It's my main job, if that's what you're asking, and yes, I do make a decent living from it. At the end of the day, I've got quite a few years left in me yet.'

'Hun, how old are you exactly?' I asked, suddenly suspicious.

'Twenty-three. Why? How old are you?'

Fuck, I was well shocked. I never go out with someone younger than me, not even a month younger. A three-year difference! I am all up for women having toy boys if that's their thing, but it's just so ageing. I mean, Madonna looks like her boyfriends' nan. And I don't want to be all jel of my boyfriend's youth. I tried not react and just said calmly, 'Twenty-six.'

'Nah, fuck off you are! I thought you were twenty-one. Well, babe, if Lewis Hamilton could screw an older bird like Nicole Scherzinger, then I don't see what's stopping us.' Awww, he was already comparing us to racing royalty! Let's face it, there was now a vacancy.

He then told me what he raced, where he raced and when he raced. Don't ask me any details cos I haven't a clue – I know that he wasn't F1 yet, but that was his ambition, which he believed he was very close to securing. It's funny, though, how racing is all about supercars and podiums and champagne, and so is Essex. The inventor of motorsports must have been a local. But I picked up everything he said about his income. Basically, he was already minted cos he had minted parents. But he still had to get sponsorship, which meant charming the arse off rich people.

Don't go thinking I'm a gold-digger, because I really don't need to be. It's the sweet smell of success that draws me in every time and money just happens to be a by-product of that. Did I mention he did part-time modelling? All in all, this was shaping up nicely. In my head I was rubbing my hands together, then rubbing those hands all over his ripped bod.

After dinner, we went upstairs where there was some woman singing by the piano. Only saw bloody Ray Winstone and his wife up there! Ben ordered me another glass of Cristal, but he stopped drinking because he was driving. This happens a lot on Essex dates, believe it or not. Our love for arriving and leaving places in a flash car outweighs our love for alcohol. Now, I can't remember much else from that night apart from pure lust. We couldn't have been sat any closer unless I'd been on his lap. I kept touching his leg and his eyes kept flickering down to my boobs.

Eventually, he went, 'Babe, are you going to kiss me or what?'

I would love to say our first kiss was sensual and romantic, with the champagne, the music and Ray Winstone eyeballing us, but it was more like an erotic explosion rippling through my body. I wanted him so bad, but I was not going to break my own first date rule. I've come too far in life to start doing that. So despite his best attempts, I told him I had to get up at 6 a.m. the next morning. Like I've ever gotten up at 6 a.m. So when he dropped me off, we got it on a bit more in the car, but I dragged myself out after twenty minutes.

Always got to leave them wanting more.

You Gotta Fake It to Make It

I managed to give everyone a breakdown on the previous night's events as I was getting ready for work the next morning. Brooke was as modest as ever and claimed her styling had made me irresistible. She made me go into details such as did he pay (he did), did he have a hard-on in the car (he did), and did he have a hot mate for her (he didn't). Then I phoned Gemma, who gushed about what my wedding would be like. Then I called Ryan, who just put fear into me.

'So he's hot, yeah?' asked Ryan.

'Yeah.'

'But he's not got a home gym, no?'

'No.'

'Oh good, so you can tell me what gym he goes to and I'll check him out for you, yeah?'

'Yeah. I mean no!' It's so confusing the way he ends questions with the answer he wants to hear.

'Well, don't say I don't do you any favours, hun.'

While we were talking a text came through. Ben had sent me a topless picture of himself from some magazine shoot and he'd written underneath, *Just in case you'd forgotten me. Amazing night babe, we'll do it again soon xx.* Now, this picture was like something you see on the front of *Attitude* magazine.

'Oh my God, Ryan. He's just sent me such a fit picture of himself, but it's pretty gay. Hang on, I'm just going to forward it to you. Tell me what you think.'

There was an *X Factor*-type pause until Ryan broke the tension by screaming, 'Oh my God, he's so hot, especially with his hand reaching into his pants like that. I'd totally do him.'

'That wasn't actually what I asked you to comment on. Do you think he could be a bit gay?'

'A homoerotic picture don't make him gay, hun. And if he is bi, then two can play that game.'

That's mine and Ryan's dream, that we find some bloke we both fancy and he's like our love slave. It's so rare we fancy the same bloke that this will never happen. Let's just say that as Ryan gets older, the boys he does don't. He loves his twinkies. And because he's hot in a Herculean kind of way (dark blond hair, ridiculously good cheekbones, biceps as big as my head), he can totally get away with it. When the age gap starts to look too weird, I'll take him aside and have a word in his ear. Like he'll care.

'I honestly don't care if he is bi,' I continued, 'but I'd just want him to tell me if he was. I blame you for putting thoughts in my head. Everyone who fancies you on Grindr always seems to have a wife or girlfriend. You've messed with my head, babe.'

'Hun, if it makes you feel any better I will totally tell you if I spot him on Grindr.' Isn't it so cool that there's a GPS to find your nearest gay?

Grindr is well necessary because there are so many well-dressed, tanned pretty boys walking round West Essex, it's really hard to work out who's what. Grindr just cuts out the crap and goes, 'This one's up for it.' And because of Ryan's antics with the 'straights' he finds on Grindr, I've realized there's a lot of men out there who keep telling themselves that loving cock is a fetish instead of an orientation. And I totally get that it's hard to come out. I mean, at one point Ryan was so far in the closet he was practically touching Narnia. Whenever we were walking down Loughton High Street as teenagers, I'd innocently say to him, 'Do you fancy any girls here?' Guaranteed he'd point one out who was wearing a baseball cap, sunglasses, a white vest top and tight jeans. So basically the boyishly dressed girl whose face you can't see behind the hat and shades. But like all Essex men, Ryan still loves boobs. He claims it's 'not in a sexual way' but in a 'comforting way'. That's worse, if you ask me.

'Hun, I don't mean to worry you, but this bloke is ripped. If you want to hold on to him, you're going to have to match him in the body stakes,' Ryan blurted out, just as I was starting to feel more positive about Ben.

'What d'you mean, you bitch?'

'I get these types in the gym all the time, and they're always moaning that their girlfriends don't work out and that it's a turn-off. And I'm not just saying that because I'm a body fascist. If you want to hold on to buff blokes like Mark Wright, they need their physical match, don't they, yeah? That's why he could never marry Lauren, yeah?'

'I go to the gym,' I said defensively.

'Using the sauna doesn't count, hun. You know you've got an amazing body, but I've always said a little bit of toning would take you to Jennifer Aniston's league.'

Ryan is a personal trainer and has got many Z-list celebs in shape, but I'd always knocked back his offers because I've never enjoyed pain. But I couldn't fight it any longer, not if I was playing with the big boys now.

'Fine. I'll lift some weights if it makes you happy.'

'Hun, this will be so exciting! We're going to totally transform you,' Ryan screeched. 'Meet you at Virgin Active after work, yeah?'

Before I knew it, I'd become Ryan's special project. He's so convincing sometimes. But see, this was the problem. I totally started listening to other people like they knew what I needed if I was going to go out with a racing driver. But thinking about it, why would they?

We'd only dealt in premiership footballers before, and they're a piece of piss.

※

I hardly heard from Ben in the next fortnight, but it's not like he was my boyfriend. He wasn't even around Essex because the racing season was about to begin, so he'd gone off with his team to do meetings and test races somewhere fancy. Didn't matter to me because I was selling the shit out of wedding dresses. The only reason Tash and I work well together is because we now respect the different strengths we bring to the business. Mine is shopping and selling, hers is customer service. I'm in my absolute element at a wedding fair. I swear it's like working a market stall. You just got to look glamorous and keep talking to someone until you're best mates. If things are quiet, I'll put on a dress and pretend to be a customer prancing around in front of the mirror. I've got a gift for making clothes look good so I may as well use it. Tasha gets well nervous in case customers feel they've been tricked, so she makes me say that I work for the shop but this stunning dress is new in and I just had to try it on. Whatever. Tasha used to call it my 'dummy' act, but she soon shut up when sales rocketed. Giving me commission for each sale was the smartest thing she ever did.

I'd been giving up every single Sunday to flog her wares recently, and as a result I'd beaten my quarterly PB (that's Personal Best to you). When you have success like that, you really don't give a shit about a bloke you've had one date with. Instead, you go treat yourself to a new dress and your boss gives you a bottle of bubbly because your mum told her to.

But there was one thing getting in my way of going all out with the celebrations, and that was Ryan. I wouldn't recommend hiring friends to assist with personal trans-formations, that's all I'm saying. He totally dissed my diet regime, which is ridiculous cos it had worked just fine for me so far. We call it 'Shit Yourself Thin'. You simply eat loads of sugar-free Polos and the pounds drop off. The only downer is you can't leave the safety of your bathroom while you're on it. So I was perfectly in control of my body, but that wasn't enough for Ryan. He wanted to make me over like some Barbie doll, but one that's all sweaty and angry. Then we'd go for a drink afterwards like we'd never had a cross word between us. It was pretty emotional being gym bitches.

Our main arguments were about when to go to the gym and what to do when I was there. All gym machines made me want to up-chuck, so we resorted to Power Plate, which would have been alright if it weren't for him shouting, 'Tighten up and breathe'. How you meant to do both at the same time? I refused to do swimming as it would ruin my hair. I tried a Zumba class down Queens Road but I can't follow dance routines. I can't help it if I'm a freestyler. But we finally found something I was born to do: kick-boxing. Ryan even got me these gorgeous pink Lonsdale boxing gloves. Turns out I pack a real punch.

As I was going out in public after our workouts, I would spend ages in the changing rooms doing myself up. I swear Ryan thinks I wake up like this. I would see the same women in there day in, day out, and we'd all be in there for hours swapping make-up, tonging hair, talking shit. I mean, I only did it for a few months, but this was these women's full-time job. As Mum is her own boss, she dips in and out of the health club social scene, but usually she goes down David Lloyd in Chigwell. It's an older crowd there, wandering around in sports gear and chittering away. People are lunching and carrying around tennis rackets, but I swear they don't know where the courts are. Nice life if you want it.

So once I'd said my goodbyes to the changing-room girls, we'd take our cars down the King Will. You might think, what's Becci doing down an old boy boozer? But the King William IV, to give it its proper title, is a classic example of a West Essex pub. The interior is white, cream and bleached wood and it's got a gorgeous outside bit so you can tan as you drink. The only shitter is that bloody Jack Tweed is always down there when I am. Straight after Jade Goody's funeral he was there. Straight after one of his many assault trials, he was there. Straight after waking up, he was there.

So anyway, Ryan and me would spend most of the time moaning about our love lives over a bottle of rosé. Truth is we were both looking for the same thing: a successful bloke to radically shake up our lives. But we were too proud to admit this to each other. I mean, I'd been single for over two years by that point and Ryan had never had a boyfriend. Don't go thinking either of us was sex-starved, though. We'd both been with men who nearly got the boyfriend title, but there was always a major flaw which meant they never quite made it. I'm sorry, but I've seen some people (my sister) settle for second best just because their ovaries were clanging. Me and Ryan have standards; so shoot us.

It was while we were at one of our post-gym King Will sessions that I got my first text from Ben after a nine-day silence. Oh yeah, he was all about personal appearances before, but now texting was suddenly acceptable. Clearly Ben was all about playing games, but he'd met his match. Our conversation went like this:

HIM: What you doing this Saturday night, babe?
ME: Sorry, who is this?
HIM: It's Ben.

ME: Sorry hun, hadn't saved your number.
HIM: So do you want to go to a charity night this
    Saturday? Woolston Manor.
Me: Not if it's boxing.

You might think that's a weird response, but seriously, I've been to so many charity boxing matches
round here it's obscene.

HIM: Nah babe, it's a fashion show and party.
ME: Yer, then defo.
HIM: Pick you up in a taxi.
ME: Cool. Laters, hun.

I was well pleased with that, but Ryan said I'd been
cold and it was an epic fail on the flirting front. But I
couldn't do flirting because I didn't know where I stood
in his game. Ryan just doesn't get the way us breeders
operate.

Live Large, Roll High

I was right to be cautious because when the cab rocked up on Saturday night, Ben was there but so was his manager. You know, the guy who was shopping for girls at One9Five. I've genuinely forgotten his name so I'll just keep on calling him Gino. So when I saw Ben in the back and Gino in the front, I felt a bit deflated.

'Alright, babe,' said Ben as I got in. 'You remember Gino, don't you?'

'Yeah, how could I forget.'

'Hello, Becci. Can I just say, I love that dress you're almost wearing,' Gino said with the most intense stare. Such a sleaze. I was wearing a seriously short dress that night, but I wasn't about to hide the results of my work-out hell. I had put a gold shimmer oil all down my legs so they looked unbelievable. I was wearing this red dress which clung to every curve and at the back there was a zip that went all the way from top to bottom. Brooke was with me when I bought it, and she said it was the kind of dress just asking to be unzipped. Duh! That was the point! I also had this fab black and white snakeskin bag and I was wearing black Armani shoes which have a huge bow on the front. I suppose I had gone for a pretty sexy look, but that Gino could bog right off. If you've got it, flaunt it.

'You look as fit as fuck, babe,' said Ben, pulling me towards him for a full-on pash. That was more like it.

'Thanks, hun. Don't look so bad yourself.' I really had to contain myself because he was wearing this grey suit with a grey waistcoat, white shirt and black tie. I can't even begin to tell you what that does to me. It was so David Beckham. If I'm about to have sex with a man wearing a suit, I won't let him take it off. We've all got our quirks, but mine's a bit more dangerous. That's why I can't work at the Stock Exchange. I'd be some sort of raging nympho.

If there's a wedding fair at Woolston Manor, you'll almost definitely find me there, so it felt like a bit of a treat going to an actual do. Although another fashion show so soon after Essex Fashion Week wasn't lighting my fire. Now, that had been a right laugh. I mean, I'd seen Lydia off *TOWIE* dressed in a cling-film outfit, I'd seen Jessica's bad hair extensions because I was sat behind her, I'd seen a dog fashion show, drunk from a champagne fountain and got my picture taken with Nanny Pat. What's better than that? It's mental all the attention and perks lavished on the TOWIE lot now. I know a few local salons offer free treatments to people like Jessica and Nanny Pat and the rest of the TOWIE lot in exchange for a bit of publicity via Twitter. But then Gemma heard through the grapevine that some of the girls started taking the piss and asking if stylists could come over to the house all the time to give blow-dries before a night out. The TOWIE publicity monster can get out of control round here sometimes, but you got to keep your business head on and know when their patronage has stopped doing you any favours. You just have to look at the TOWIE tweets to see all the stuff the girls are blagging. I'd totally be doing that if I was them, though, because I'm just as shameless.

Just as I heard my favourite sound, the popping of corks, I suddenly felt a bit uneasy. I turned round to see why I had a burning sensation on my back, and there was Bucket giving me the once-over. What gives with that girl? I wish she'd bloody move counties. She seemed to be wearing a really weird silver dress, which is when I realized she was actually in the fashion show. She may have been modelling, but I consider that work. Meanwhile, I was on a date with a ridiculously good-looking racing driver. I thought, up your bloody bum, Bucket. It's like she heard, because her eyes went really squinty with rage.

'Babe, I've got to chat up some potential sponsors. You'll be alright on your own, won't you, sweet cheeks?'

'Yeah, no worries. But I'd hurry up if I were you. Some hot-shot fashion designer might whisk me off to Milan.'

'Babe, it's a fashion show for a shop in Loughton.'

'Yeah, but still . . .' I didn't bother finishing my sentence because he'd already gone. I'd lost my date for a bit, but it was fine because he sent a glass of champagne my way which was nicely done, so he was back in my good books.

I'm pretty good at talking to everyone and anyone, so I scanned the room for a victim. Sat at a table was Chloe Sims and her cousin Joey Essex, who were at that point newcomers to the show. And yes, his surname really is Essex, although he wasn't actually born in Essex so it's not all that neat. As with everyone in West Essex, Chloe clamoured to get a part in the second series of *TOWIE* and got a starring role. And with her teeth too! Seriously, she could eat an apple through a letterbox with those gnashers. It doesn't help that she had them bleached proper white and got lip fillers to complete the look. And her boobs are out of control. She looks like a real-life Picasso painting. I'm sorry, but I can't hold in what I see. And I feel bad because she's a really lovely person and she was there with her daughter, so I could see she was an amazing mum too. In fact, you remember Chloe's wedding-themed thirtieth birthday? The flower girl was Madison, but I love the fact Chloe never exposes her to the cameras. She's very protective of her.

I only sat with them for a few minutes before she was dragged off for some photos, but from what I remember, she was talking about some older bloke in the show they were trying to make a romantic storyline out of which I now realize was Mick Norcross. She didn't seem that bothered about the producers telling her what to do and who to do. Why would you when you're being handed a new career on a plate? I mean, the fact Jessica Wright snogged Joey Essex just shows there's no limit when it comes to creating a romantic storyline. What next? Lydia's mum and Mario? Do me a favour.

I spotted Joey Essex joining her for a picture. So skinny! His hair should be in the Museum of Essex, it's so finely crafted. Me and the girls call that style the Brentwood Bouffant, and I got to admit, I've got a thing for it. Gemma thinks blokes with it look like 'a dandy', so I think she's saying it's a bit gay. I say the look is like Danny from *Grease* or James Dean, you know – all 1950s, but bigger and better. Gemma and I have a lot of arguments about the bouffant, so I'll stop there.

Ben eventually found me and introduced me to all the Flash Harries he'd been talking to. Some bloke who ran a restaurant chain, some bloke that did banking, some bloke who did property. I didn't really listen because I was now quite drunk, and Ben was looking at me in a funny way. He then just gabbled away at me without stopping for breath. Proper wired. Like, when they came round with raffle tickets, he just went mental and bought a whole book. Someone had been at the gak. If there's one drug an Essex man doesn't need, it's one that makes him gobbier and louder, but for some reason it's the drug of choice round here. But if I think about it, I was drawn to Charlie when he was off his face on coke, so maybe I've got a thing for coke-heads? If I'm to be honest, I was liking this less suave Ben because finally I felt like the cool one. He suddenly grabbed me by the elbow and led me out the hall.

'Oi, where we going?' I said, trying to keep my heels on.

'Babe, I'm getting us out of here,' he replied, searching for the exit.

As much as I wanted to see the fashion show because I was convinced Bucket would trip up, this offer was far more enticing. So yep, I called a cab and we ran out of there so fast, it looked like we'd nicked something. I shouldn't really say that, because I later discovered that all the money raised *did* actually get nicked. Isn't that the lowest of the low? When things like that happen, I find it comforting to know that BHQ also like to get involved in these matters, so I'm pretty sure those thieves eventually got their comeuppance. BHQ aren't all bad. Especially since I was about to have unbelievably hot sex with the best body in town. I didn't even notice the ride back to his because we were locked together and his hand was up my dress. I'm sure the taxi driver didn't mind getting an earful of my whimpers.

Turned out he only bloody lived in Repton Park. Does everyone live here? I was desperate to knock on Brooke's door and surprise her but there was just no time. It all got a bit frantic with zips being undone, stumbling out of underwear in his hallway and limbs everywhere. Before I knew it, his suit was off. How gutted was I? I was tempted to ask him to put it back on but decided it was too early in our relationship to expose my fetishes. And the thing is, once I saw his ripped body, I decided it was best we did this naked. I was so hungry for him, you know when you physically can't get enough of someone? We didn't even make it upstairs the first time. Then we found the bedroom, had sex again. Then we slept for a bit. Had sex again. It was relentless.

There was one disturbing moment, though. I went in to his bathroom in the middle of the night and was snooping through his cabinets like you do. I pulled open a drawer and found it packed with sex toys and make-up. Alarm bells rang and I thought, he's got a girlfriend. But it was such a random collection of plastic bits and cheap underwear, I reckon it was stuff that women had left behind. Almost like a shagger's graveyard. I picked out something which turned out to be a vibrator. Then I thought, what if it's not been cleaned, so I threw it back in and scrubbed my hands.

I suppose some women would have been more confused by the make-up, but it's nothing I hadn't seen
before in an Essex man's house. Although, I'd only
seen that amount in my house. Like my bathroom, his
shelves were packed with face masks, scrubs and all
sorts of potions. We were proper kindred spirits. When
I got back into bed Ben went, 'You've got such soft
skin,' and I thought, 'He just wants to know what I use.'

In the morning, he totally surprised me by bringing
me a cup of tea. He just didn't look the type to make
tea. So as we were lounging about in his ridiculously
wide bed, he said, 'Babe, I'd love to spend the day with
you, but I'm playing golf with the boys in about two
hours . . .'

'Yeah, yeah, that's fine. I was about to get ready to go
anyway,' I said, spilling hot liquid on my bare leg.

'Nah, I wasn't telling you to get out. You can spend
the whole day here if you want. I'm just saying, I've
got to head out in a bit. I'd rather be in bed with you
all day, though.'

'To be honest, I don't think you've got the stamina,' I
said. I did a little cheeky smile to let him know I was
teasing. Some blokes take it all a bit too seriously, so
you got to be careful.

'Well, next time we go out, we'll see about that.'

I was deliriously happy. There would be a next time!
I celebrated with a shower. Obviously, a man like him
has a wet room. And obviously he followed me in for

one last session, even though I was feeling a bit sore by that point. I made it quick because I was so desperate to get over to Brooke's and dissect the last eighteen hours of my life. I kissed Ben goodbye for ages and then he watched me walk away, so I had to be all sexy and calm. As soon as I was out of eyeshot, I bounced over to Brooke's building.

'So he lives in one of the houses, does he?' said Brooke. 'I don't like them anyway. My flat's so much cosier.' People get so competitive about their places round here!

'And he let you stay over, did he?' Brooke asked in a totally pass-agg way. She'd been having major issues in that department. Not once in the last year had a bloke let her stay over. I'm guessing that's because all of them have been cheating on their wives and girlfriends who are due back the next day. The last one she hooked up with was definitely up to no good. She gets there, has sex, goes to the bathroom to find a stack of women's toiletries. (Yeah, I'm aware I just told you about Ben's toiletries, but that's different.) When she quizzes him, he says it belongs to his ex. Then, as they're having sex again, Brooke spots a card on one of the shelves. It says, 'Congratulations On Your Wedding'. As he's mid-thrust, Brooke goes, 'Are you married or what?'

He replies, 'No.'

She says, 'Then what's that wedding card about?', and he says, 'I was married but we've separated now.'

Fuck that shit, only newly-weds keep their cards up.

As soon as he's done, he then tells her she's got to leave because he's got golf in the morning. (Yeah, I'm also aware Ben said that too, but it doesn't stop people staying the night.) When Brooke told me this story, my heart completely sank. I suppose I'm a romantic at heart who believes you should at least let the confetti settle before banging someone else.

But this is the thing – now we're in the second half of our twenties, everyone's partnered up, so the odds of sleeping with a cheater are unbelievably high. We want it all in Essex – cosy coupledom and fast living – but those two lifestyles totally clash. I'll fess up here: Charlie and I actually split because he caught me cheating on him. There, it's out now. Our relationship had been over for months, so I suppose it was a cowardly way of breaking up with him. And that footballer that I mentioned earlier? That's the one I cheated on him with. We'd gone to an amazing country hotel together, I'd taken pictures of us in bed together, and I never deleted those pictures. Guess who used the camera next? It was a hard way for Charlie to find out, and obviously with all those steroids he was on, he hit the roof. But you live and learn, and I'd never do that to anyone again. A lot of people drag out a relationship because they're scared of being on their own, but that's pretty selfish when you think about it. I would not recommend cheating on someone just to dump them. But sometimes that's what it takes to realize the relationship's dead.

The thing is, I get major crushes on people like the footballer and I get this blindness. The passion takes over and all other facilities shut down. So when everything started kicking off with Ben, Brooke had seen it all before.

'I don't want to piss on your parade, but don't go throwing yourself head first into this,' Brooke said, trying to look all knowing.

'I'll have you know there's a lot of evidence that he might not be a shit. First off, he's got a tattoo on the inside of his arm that says "family", so he loves his family, right?'

'Nah, that would just creep me out if I saw that on a bloke's arm. It's all a bit Reggie Kray.'

'Shut up! It is not. It means he's devoted to his people. Secondly, I haven't had to spend a penny on our dates, so he's generous. Thirdly, he's amazing in bed . . .'

'Yeah, because he's had the practice,' Brooke butted in.

'Good, I'm glad he has. I don't want a virgin who's been saving himself, do I?' I replied defensively.

'I got to say, something does seem different about this. I mean, you're always overexcited after date one, but by date two you're trying to work out how to get out of it.'

'Yeah, because they never live up to how I pictured them to be. They'll do something lame like say something proper soppy or expect me to get a round in.'

'Becs, you are one of the funniest girls I've ever met. I honestly want to jump out of a window just to stop the laughter pains sometimes. But this Ben bloke is just so serious. I don't get how it works.'

'Yeah, cos he's putting on a front, isn't he. It's like how Charlie's a right laugh but he can't be mucking around when he's guarding the entrance to the VIP Lounge. All sorts would be getting in then. You've only seen Ben's public side, but he's much softer when it's just the two of us.'

Brooke was clearly bored of me droning on about Ben, so she grabbed a marker pen and wrote 'family' on my arm. I wasn't impressed. I grabbed the marker pen and wrote 'minge' on her foot. We laughed so hard I honestly pissed myself a bit. I once told Brooke that Amanda Seyfried off that *Mamma Mia!* film had 'minge' tattooed on her foot because Colin Firth told her to or something, and we had a major fight because she said I was making shit up as always. We didn't talk for about a week. You know you're best friends when you're able to have these blazing rows because it means they feel like a sister to you.

Tattoos are generally a sore point between us because when I got my feather tattoo on my lower back, we had a huge bust-up. She claimed I had stolen her tattoo idea and then she called it a 'tramp stamp'. That's what you call proper jel behaviour.

And she got more jel as the days went on because I was spending all my time with Ben. I suppose she'd got used to us being a double-act, so I don't think she was very happy for me. I couldn't help that, though, could I? I mean, she was always jetting here and there, so it wasn't like she didn't have a life. But she'd send me a lot of pass-agg texts like, *fort u mite b bz . . . wil buk tan 4 1*, or *whr u gon? . . . wd b gr8 2 c u*. That sort of stuff. And those are word-for-word texts. Takes me bloody ages to work them out.

And I was busy out and about at Ben's events. He had two test races in April which I went to watch. I think he came second in both, but there was no question, he was an incredible driver. He had no fear on the road and no self-doubt off the road. I won't deny it, seeing him race was a major turn-on. He was all kitted up in his racing gear and he'd look all brooding when he took off his helmet and gloves. Men doing dangerous things and taking off helmets is my thing. It's the same reason I love the film *Top Gun* so much.

But it was really Ben's focus that made me so hot for him. He was more disciplined than any footballer when it came to his lifestyle. Ryan was so right about Ben's workout regime. He went to the gym nearly every day, so thanks to him, I was able to spend time with Ben down the Repton Park gym. And he seriously monitored his diet – it was all about the protein. He didn't really get drunk either, and he wasn't really a coke-head, just every now and then. He was just so in control of himself because he was hungry for success. When you see first-hand what these footballers get up to in clubs, it's no wonder the England team are so shit.

The best thing about these races were the overnight stays in these amazing hotels where I spent most of my time in bed or in a hot tub. That's my kind of week-end. Some evenings we did more of the hob-nobbing, like in Woolston Manor. He'd gained a lot of sponsors so it showed how seductive he could be to both men and women.

But we were kind of weird when it came to our friends. Like he wouldn't come out with my lot and I wouldn't hang out with his. I mean, for all I know he was taking other women home with him. Considering the circumstances I met him under, I'd have been sur-prised if he wasn't. I was no angel either and indulged in a few cheeky snogs, but I can't handle dating two men at once, not after the affair experience. It's just proper time-consuming.

So why was I bothering with Ben if I had his card marked? Simply because I was enjoying life with him in it. Just so you can fully grasp *how* much fun the two of us had together, let me tell you about the Mayfair experience.

When Kate and Wills got married – you know, *the*

royal wedding – there was a lot of love around. I kept banging on about how London would be the place to be that day, so Ben surprised me with a stay at the Hilton Park Lane and an afternoon of shopping on his card followed by drinks and dinner at the Mayfair Hotel.

Wait, though, it gets even better. At dinner, he gave me my favourite kind of blue box. No, it wasn't a ring but this gorgeous Tiffany double-hearted diamond necklace I'd spotted earlier in the day. In my eyes, if a bloke gives you a gift for no reason *and* he's actually heard your shopping hint, it means he really wants to make you happy. My sister's husband Tony buys her a new wedding ring every anniversary. She never likes them, but she always expects them. Where's the romance in that? She even gives them names, so there's gym wedding ring, holiday wedding ring, night wedding ring and wedding ring. She only really loves the original. My gift from Ben meant more than all her silly rings put together. Considering I'd been beautifying myself for four days and had avoided carbs for the same amount of time, I'd say an expensive Tiffany necklace was about right. I didn't want the night to end after dinner, so Ben suggested we hit a club called Aura just around the corner.

As with all restaurants and clubs we'd been to, Ben seemed to know everyone at Aura, including Jonny Dodge, one of the owners, who is well fit but short. Looks weirdly like a stockier and posher Joey Essex. Turns out he's the man to know in motor sport if you like to have a good time around Grand Prix season. Some people got shoved off some seats so we could sit at the table (I should say I felt terrible but I didn't), and then Ben ordered a magnum of champagne which I thought was a bit much for just the two of us, but then I realized he'd done it to impress not just me but the entire club. Everyone knows when you've ordered a magnum here. The music shuts down, wild west gun shots and horns are played and the spotlight goes on the flash Harry. Why's nobody doing this in Essex? It'd go down a storm if you were given props every time you splashed serious cash.

So anyway, Kate's wedding reception may have been kicking off in Buckingham Palace, but there was only one princess in town that night. The champagne was flowing and I danced with everyone and anyone. Ben doesn't do dancing, just intense watching, so when I saw him coming over to me on the dance floor, I didn't know what to think. Then he just walked behind me, wrapped his arms around my waist and went, 'I want to fuck you right here, right now.' I mean, it was seriously hot.

We tried to go in the toilets, but those bloody toilet attendants are everywhere these days, so in the end we made our way up Piccadilly, stopping for a quick fumble on every dark street corner until we got back to the Hilton. I don't do walking, so that just shows how off my face I was. I don't think we even had sex when we got back because I seem to remember waking up in my new pink bandeau dress. Or maybe we did. But I do remember waking up in *the* most luxurious bed I'd ever been in. Imagine sleeping on a thick duvet with another duvet on top. I've actually recreated this bed in my own place, it was that life-changing. But anyway, we had a late checkout, so we just chilled, ordered food, watched *Friends*.

I didn't want the day to end, but Essex was calling.

7

Say No to the Semi-Pro

I'd had seven missed calls from Gemma while I'd been hitting the town. Obviously I couldn't call her while I was making the most of my London high life. When Ben finally dropped me home late Saturday afternoon, I called her as soon as I'd kicked my heels off. When she picked up, she was sobbing, but it was angry sobbing. Way worse than when her eyelashes fell out.

'Where've you been?'

'Up town with Ben. What's going on, hun?'

'Why have you been ignoring my calls? I needed you,' Gemma said with more shallow sobs.

'Hun, I'm here now. Talk to me.'

'It's so awful, Becci. I don't know what to do. Grant's done it again.' I knew what this meant. He'd cheated on her again.

'How did you find out?' I asked.

'*She Facebooked me, the bitch,*' she yelled. This was the

most furious I'd ever heard her. 'She wrote, "I know you've been seeing my boyfriend. I've seen the texts. Fuck off and get your own bloke." Can you fucking believe the cheek? So I replied, "Who the hell are you? I'm engaged to Grant and live with him. Pretty sure that makes him my boyfriend, you stupid cow. How long you been seeing him?" Then she didn't reply to that.'

'Good one, Gem. Who the hell does this girl think she is?'

'I know! I just can't believe this bitch found me on Facebook to warn me off him. It's so humiliating.'

'So have you seen Grant?' I asked

'I told him not to bother coming home last night. But he came round this morning and tried talking to me through the letterbox. I just didn't want to hear his shit. And he had a black eye.'

'Hit by a girl, I reckon. The shame,' I said, trying to make her feel better.

'And he's gone to stay with Charlie.'

'That's what best men are for.'

Grant and Charlie had been best mates at the Catholic school next door to Essex Hogwarts. Same school that Arg went to, but they were a few years above. We met them from hanging out at the bus stop after school. I didn't even need to get the bus home, but this hotspot was where the romances began. So Gem started going out with Grant in the last year of school, but I didn't get with Charlie until the summer I finished uni. The problem was, once Charlie and I became an item, the four of us got a bit too cliquey. Nothing worse than regular double dates in my view. And those boys were so loyal to each other, Charlie would never let on about Grant's cheating or give me any details. I respected Charlie for that because I so would have run straight to Gem.

'Where's Brooke, anyway?' I asked.

'She's on the way back from Ibiza but she's about tonight. Please come over. I need you both here.'

'You don't even need to ask. But we're not sitting about moping. We're going down Sugar Hut, hun.'

'I don't know if I can.'

'You've got to, Gem. It's the only way through this. When we're banging back our first Sambuca, you'll know it makes sense.'

I was a little bit worried that Brooke would be a bit off with me because I'd only seen her once in the whole of April, but she was totally happy to see me. I think she might have been doing my own technique back at me, which is to kill people with kindness. And it worked, because the nicer she was, the guiltier I felt. It did cross my mind I'd become a boys' girl. I decided I was going to make amends for my absence and give the girls my full attention that night. I wouldn't even text Ben.

Gemma perked up as soon as she clocked my new Tiffany necklace. She's one of those girls that has proper happiness if something good's happened to her mates. Brooke made a comment loaded with sarcasm, something like, 'What did you have to do to get that then?' She was just jel, as always.

I don't think I've told you about the first time I met Gemma and Brooke, but it's very telling of all our natures. Me, Gemma and Ryan met at school when we were eleven. One day, early on in the first term, a very little Gemma stood at the front of our class and held up a quid. She then said, 'I just found this pound by the lockers. Has anyone lost it?'

I immediately piped up, 'Yep, that's definitely my pound.'

It wasn't. But the lovely trusting Gemma passed it over to a horrible deceitful me, and from then on we were bosom buddies. I was a shyster at such a young age.

I don't have a first memory of Ryan – he was just always there, the centre of attention. But he was so tiny and skinny back then, with glasses. You wouldn't even recognize him if I showed you a picture. Then I met Brooke at university. I went to Liverpool because I'd read it had the best social scene of any university. I was not disappointed. Turns out the ladies of Liverpool have exactly the same attitude to life as the Essex girl, but they'd easily beat us in a fight. It was so *Desperate Scousewives*. Brooke was in my halls and, being the friendly person I am, I went to each room to introduce myself. I knocked on Brooke's door and heard a noise.

I opened the door to find her lying on her bed reading a magazine. She just looked at me like I was a piece of shit. I muttered, 'Alright? Just thought I'd say hello. I'm in the room two doors down from you.' She replied, 'Yeah, OK,' and went back to reading her magazine. How rude is that! But that's Brooke. You've got to earn her respect before she gives anything of herself.

We both did Business Studies, but I wouldn't say the subject was in the forefront of our minds. Some bloke came huffing into class once and went, 'Shit, have you heard about the share crisis?' and I went, 'Oh my God, what's happened to Cher?' People did not get tired of taking the piss out of me for that one.

We were considered pretty exotic in this sea of northerners, so we learnt early on that standing out from the crowd got us things. I won't lie, we ate men for breakfast in more ways than one. You could say we crafted our skills with the Liverpool players. Brooke did get chlamydia, though, so that was a bit of a downer in the promiscuous years. After uni we saved Brooke from a life in Billericay and got her to move to the Golden Triangle. Best thing she ever did. I knew Brooke and Gemma would get on despite their differences. If anything, Gemma brings out the best in Brooke. I think that's why on this night out Brooke was on top form, because we were both desperate to put a smile back on Gem's face. The thought of anyone hurting her just made us fume.

Four hours and three bottles of champagne later, we found ourselves outside the mighty Sugar Hut. Now I got to say, it was the first time I'd been here since the second series of TOWIE had kicked off, and I was shocked. There'd always been queues, but nothing like this so early on. The club was firing on all cylinders that month, what with the show being back on and nominated for a BAFTA as well as the launch of Joey Essex's Sunday night Reem party. We'd nearly come the week before when the club put on a night to celebrate Kirk's birthday, but my cousin Russ texted to say don't bother coming. It was rammed with people hoping to see the cast of TOWIE. People like Russ. Such a plum.

Judging by the queue of people, this night wasn't looking much better. Seemed to be a load of hen and stag dos. I suppose people think it's a laugh to come along and release their inner-Essex. A lot of women think they have to wear the shortest skirt possible when they come here, and good for them if they're having a laugh and putting money in the Essex wallet. A true Essex girl knows how to stay on the right side of sexy, though.

Anyway, the TOWIE tourists were none of my concern as I zoned in on the doorman, who I knew through Charlie. As usual, we were straight in. And this is one place you need to be in VIP to have a good night. You're all packed in like cattle if you go to the main club now.

The only space is downstairs where the old club tunes play, but who wants to hear that apart from my sister?

We pushed past all the trashy WEGs hovering around the VIP rope, and as soon as Kirk's older brother Dan spotted us, he came over to get us. He's the spit of Mick. Pretty sweet since we hadn't been there for months. There were a lot of new people in VIP who I didn't recognize. The new kids can take your place pretty fast round here. We'd barely sat down on the white couches before a bottle of champagne landed on the table and the blokes were swarming around us. I got talking to one who claimed he was a doctor like in that show *House*. Like he was some sort of medical detective. What a load of billy bullshit. I made my excuses and got up to find the girls, when I saw two shocking things. Some bird was undoing some bloke's flies on the dance floor to give him a handjob. Like that was going to do the Essex image any good. Then I turned round to see Gemma snogging the face off some tall skinny bloke. What was everybody on?

'Oi, Gem, what are you playing at?' I said, pulling her away from this fella she'd locked tongues with.

'Having fun. Still got it,' she slurred back at me.

'I meant for us girls to have fun tonight. I didn't mean go snogging blokes. Chicks before dicks, babe.'

'I'm single, can do what I want,' she said back to me.

'Sorry, love, you are?' said the gangly bloke. Well rude.

'I'm her best friend and she doesn't know what she's doing.'

'Yer I do,' interrupted Gemma. 'This is Kev and he's a semi-pro golfer.'

'And you're cock-blocking me,' piped up this Kev bloke.

'Gemma, listen to him. He's a lemon. And he's a semi-pro! What have I told you about this, yeah? They're all semi-pro, remember?'

'I don't give a fuck. I'm having fun so let me get back to it.'

'Yeah, just do one, love,' was Kevin's contribution.

'I'll do you *in* if you don't watch it, arsehole.' But the dick didn't hear me because he was back to groping Gemma.

It was so early on yet it had all gone so wrong. And I'd totally lost Brooke. She wasn't even in VIP. I tapped Gemma on the shoulder.

'Not you again,' said the chump, pushing me away.

'Oh, charming. I want to talk to Gemma.'

'What is it?' Gemma said, swaying towards me.

'I've had enough. Can I have your keys so I can go back to yours?' I said sternly.

'You're going?'

'Yeah, I'm bored. Everything's different and this club is stupid.'

'Where's Brooke?'

'Still here. I'll text her to say I'm off and that she has to come home with you.'

She gave me the keys, shrugged and got back to it. I felt like I was in a nightmare I couldn't wake up from. It took me so long to get past all the try-hards and down the stairs that by the time I got outside, I'd completely lost my rag. I got a taxi easily since it wasn't even midnight and headed for Epping. Meanwhile, I'd got a text back from Brooke saying, *'I've pulled. Not coming back to Gems.'* What could I do except text Gem that she had to make her own way home. I was beyond caring at this point. Especially when I got back to Gem's to find a drunk Grant slumped on the doorstep. I kicked him with my foot and he stirred slightly.

'Grant, you bell-end. Wake up.'

'Gem?'

'Nah, it's Becci.'

'I need Gemma. Talk to her for me.'

'You have seriously messed up this time. You couldn't even stay faithful four months before your wedding?'

'You don't understand.'

'Hun, do I look like I give a tom-tit?' I can be well harsh sometimes. But I didn't have the heart to tell him where and what Gemma was up to. I opened the door and let him in. It was his home after all. Then he just collapsed on the couch and I left him there. Turned him on his side, though, in case he choked on his own vomit. Whatever he'd done, he didn't deserve that.

The next day was well bizarre. Grant wanted to know where Gemma was. I just said he'd have to ask her, but I could see he had figured it out. To be honest, she probably wanted him to know she'd cheated on him because you just want to dish back the pain and make it a level playing field again. I had to get him out the house and back to Charlie's so Gem wouldn't know I'd let him in. It was like being on the Jerry Springer show, having to hide one cheating partner from another cheating partner because it would be explosive when they clapped eyes on each other. My thought of the day would be: don't propose to someone if you can't stop chasing skirt because you're clearly not ready.

Grant told me he'd done nothing with this mentalist girl except snog her down Funky Mojoe's. I didn't buy it, for her to have decked him one, that was the rage of a lover. Trust him to get it on with a skank down the ghetto bar too. If you're looking for somewhere to get stabbed in West Essex, this is your place. He claimed he'd done it because he gets so jealous of Gemma. I don't get that warped logic, but what do I know about their relationship? Personally, I blame the football team mentality. Grant plays for a Sunday League team much like Mark Wright plays for Essex United. I don't doubt for one second that Grant is completely in love with

Gemma, but when those boys are out together, they suddenly act like they're all single.

Anyway, I decided BHQ had dished out enough shit on Grant because his cheating had gained him a total bunny-boiler with a good right hook. Once I'd got rid of Grant I drove straight over to Ben's. There's nothing like submerging yourself in another person to dissolve all other dramas. I didn't even bother looking in on Brooke.

＊

I made sure I alternated my time between Gemma and Ben in those following weeks. She had basically told Grant to move out, but she hadn't called off the wedding, so we were in a bit of a limbo. I'd already booked the hen do in Puerto Banus, but I didn't bother to cancel it because, wedding or no wedding, we all needed a weekend of drinking and sunbathing.

Normally Gemma would be riddled with guilt about sleeping with another bloke, but there was none of that. Instead she was saying things like, 'I've lost a part of myself being with Grant,' and 'I'm too young to settle down.' I'd never seen her have a crisis like this. She was convinced she'd stopped making an effort with herself, but as I pointed out, she wouldn't be getting into VIP with us if that was the case. However, West Essex is the worst place to be if you're feeling underdressed, so even though I didn't agree with her, I knew where she was coming from. We'd always been really sure of ourselves, but these were confusing times.

I wasn't about to let us lose our way with all these stupid shenanigans, so I booked me and Gem in for massages and facials at Harmony. When you feel someone's looking after you, you feel instantly better. A lot of people don't stop to think about this and get weighed down by all the shit BHQ throw at them, but they can't touch you in a beauty salon. That's the place you build yourself up again.

I knew Ryan would make me feel guilty for chilling out in Harmony as it's a stone's throw from the gym, so I got him a couple of treatments too to stop him hassling me. You know what they say – keep your friends close and your fitness instructor closer. Although he still had the cheek to whine that the massages weren't as good since Amy Childs had left. In fact, a lot of the male clients have said that. It was so funny when TOWIE kicked off cos everyone went mental trying to find Amy's salon, which didn't even exist back then. I remember they once shot Amy giving a spray-tan at Belles & Beaus and the phone was off the hook with people trying to book a session with her. The salon got some very nice business out of it. I mean, they still love Amy at Harmony and she's there all the time getting treatments, but they must be wanting a piece of the action. Although the salon owner's daughter, Jade, is now employed as Amy's personal stylist. She used to have a hundred people following her on Twitter, but once Amy announced who her stylist was, Jade gained fifteen hundred new fans within twenty-four hours. So it all worked out in the end, right? And Amy's got her salon in Brentwood so we can all breathe easy now.

Before our treatments, we decided to go sit in the saunas so our bodies and pores were all loosened up. Only amateurs don't warm up their skin before a treatment. So anyways, we were all lying down and chilling when my phone went. I wasn't going to go in there without my iPhone, was I? To be honest, I don't normally do that, but I'd had a text from Ben saying he was going to call me with an exciting proposition. You wouldn't leave your phone in the changing rooms if you had that hanging over you, would you?

'Babe, what you doing the last weekend in May?' he said. He was sounding laid-back as usual, so I had to calm the keenness in my voice too.

'Err, not sure. Is that the bank holiday weekend?'

'Probably. You fancy coming to Monaco?'

'Where's that?'

'France, I think. Doesn't matter. It's not like you're going sightseeing. Grand Prix's on and I need a partner in crime who likes a good time.'

'Oh yeah, who you thinking of taking?' I teased.

'You, you plum. So what d'ya say, babe? You, me and some fast cars?'

'Oh my God, yes!' I said with so much keenness it's like he'd asked me to marry him.

'And there will be back-to-back parties, so bring your sexiest clothes, yeah? And lots of bikinis. This is a big fucking deal. It's the sweetest circuit there is and they know how to party.'

'I can't believe this. Will there be celebrities there? I mean proper ones, like Americans.'

'Always, babe.'

I hung up and screamed. A little tear of joy ran down my cheek.

'What's going on? What's wrong?' Ryan asked, looking all dramatic like a giant palaver was about to kick off.

'I'm going to the biggest party in the world,' I said, jumping, laughing and crying. 'I'm going to the Monaco Grand Prix.'

Ryan gasped, grabbed me and jumped up and down with me. It was a real moment. I think he was convinced that I wouldn't have got this far in the relationship process if it weren't for his torture sessions. Although when I was jumping nothing jiggled, so I suppose his work was done.

'Becs, I'm so glad everything's working out for you. You totally deserve it, hun,' said Gemma, still sitting down. I knew she was genuinely happy for me, but she was running at twenty per cent capacity at this point. I sat down and hugged her, knowing that I would make it my mission to get my girl back to a hundred per cent.

'I feel a bit light-headed,' I said, suddenly letting her go. 'I've just got to lie down for a minute.' So we lay there a bit longer chilling and Ryan and me chatted excitedly. Gemma was silent for five minutes before speaking again.

'Becs?'

'Yeah, hun?

'Can I tell you something?' she asked.

'You know you can tell me anything,' I replied.

'Yeah, but you might not like what I'm about to tell you.'

I braced myself.

'Oh God, what is it? Don't tell me, you've been looking at my boobs, haven't you? I totally know the left one's lower than the right one, though. I've been thinking about getting them done again, so don't worry. I'm totally aware.'

'No, it's about Brooke.'

'Oh? What? Has she been hating on me?'

'I think you should hear this from a friend before you see it for yourself. Plus Brooke's too scared to tell you.'

'Get it out, girl. What's happening? She's not nicked Ben off me, has she?' I laughed nervously.

'No, but she's nicked Charlie off you.' There was a pause and then she added, 'It's been going on for three weeks now.'

I lay there and thought about this. I knew I had no right to act angry cos they were both single. But I did *not* see that coming.

'Good for her,' I said eventually.

'Really?' said Gemma, sounding confused.

'Yeah, definitely. I mean, I split from Charlie two years ago. I've only ever wanted both of them to be happy and find love. I mean, it's weird, but you can't control who you fall for, right?'

'You're taking this really well, Becs. I'm so impressed with you, hun. It just shows how much you've grown up. If I'd told you this a year ago, you'd been spitting feathers. Maybe Ben's been a good influence on you after all.'

'Yeah, well we've all got to move on, haven't we? I know I have.' I had to sit up but immediately felt all dizzy again.

'Where's my phone gone?' I said, patting the seats around me.

'I can't see a thing in here,' said Ryan. 'I didn't think it possible but I've sweated out every drop of badness in my system. Let's go and get robed up for some beautifying, shall we?'

'No, but my phone,' I said, my voice getting higher. I stood up even though I was starting to feel sick and reached for the light switch hanging from the ceiling so I could see better. Turned out to be the emergency cord though, didn't it. Suddenly everyone was rushing in and trying to help me out. I spotted my phone, grabbed it, then shook off the do-gooders and just walked out in my bikini with my head held high. The other two followed, all apologetic, even though I tell them never say you're sorry and never admit you're wrong. I shrugged my shoulders to acknowledge the incident but to also say shit happens, yeah?

Although karma got me in the end, because my phone then stopped working. When I took it to get it repaired, the bloke said it was water damaged. I couldn't remember it even being near water. I was without a phone for three days!

Ryan said I'd really humiliated him in front of his colleagues that day. Well harsh. I told him to shut up, relax and enjoy his massage. I wish I'd taken my own advice because I was all stiff during mine. The massage lady said I must have a lot of worries on my shoulders. She was one hundred per cent right. I mean, that sauna incident just showed how out of it I was. The Grand Prix, the Brooke and Charlie news . . . it's a bit much getting all this breaking news while you're sweating it up in a hot box.

8

Holidays: You Bring the Heat

I had one week to get ready for Monaco! And if that wasn't bad enough, Tasha had gone on holiday with the family so I had to look after the whole shop by myself. All Saturdays from May onwards are manic as the wedding season's in full swing, so I was having to deal with all these brides whingeing during their final fittings. These women didn't know the meaning of pressure. I didn't have one single outfit to wear for the Grand Prix. I would usually call on Brooke at times like this, but I felt things were too weird. I didn't say it, but I did think it was bang out of order for my mate to get it on with my ex. Anyway, I decided Gemma needed a project to liven her up, so I got her on board Project Monaco.

I was exfoliating every other day and oiling myself up like you wouldn't believe. I brought out the big guns and drenched myself in Clarins body oils. I'm surprised I didn't slide out of bed with the amount I was slapping on each night. Then a make-up mate of Gemma's did my lash extensions for practically nothing. I went up one level too so they were that bit longer. I got my Bio Gels redone even though my last mani/pedi was only four days old. I couldn't take any risks. I got my Queens Road salon to whack in some hair extensions. Thank God I'd got my roots done recently or how would I have found the time?

On the eve of my flight I got a dark spray, then Gemma and I sped over to Bluewater to sort out my Riviera wardrobe. You probably think all Essex girls go to Lakeside. Don't get me wrong, before Bluewater existed I was all over Lakeside like it was the promised land. This is how obsessed I was when I was a teenager: one Saturday, Mum yelled up to me, 'We're going Lakeside,' and I was like, shit, they're going without me, so I got myself ready in record time. When I got downstairs, Mum was crying. What she'd actually shouted up to me was, 'Your Grandad's died.' And even though I was sad about Grandad, my heart sank when I realized there'd be no shopping that day. From then on, I was adamant I'd take driving lessons the moment I turned seventeen. The creation of Bluewater was just the icing on the cake. All a girl needs is the freedom to travel and explore new worlds.

I think shopping under pressure is more satisfying. What would you rather be: all chilled with one bag after four hours of shopping or all manic with ten bags after one hour of shopping? So for starters, I got myself a new Gossard bra. If you haven't had a boob job, this bra will make you look like you have. If you have had a boob job, this bra will push your tits up to your ears. Even the blind will see you coming.

I was going for three nights, so I bought six outfits from Reiss and Zara – that's not just for night, that's day dresses too and one jumpsuit. I don't really do high-street accessories, so I restrained myself from getting shoes in Aldo. Then I got a new pair of aviators and a new suitcase because I needed one that screamed Monaco, so I found this huge pink one. I was anxious that it was too small, but Gemma gave me a right talking-to and said it would be fine once I'd put all my make-up and hair stuff in a separate vanity case. God love that girl, she was spot on.

I bought one bikini from Ann Summers that I didn't really like, just for back-up, in case the other seven I was taking didn't work in Monaco. I was that close to buying a monokini so I'd be bang on trend, but thank God I didn't. They're well unflattering. Even Amy Childs and Maria Fowler bulged out their cut-outs. The monokini must have been invented by a proper woman hater. I'm bikinis all the way and I bought some stunning ones in Vardo when it opened. That's the boutique Chantelle from *Big Brother* opened on Queens Road. The launch day was hilarious. She arrived in a horse-drawn carriage and there was a red carpet into her shop and she had a right face on her. I got more to say about her later as I got up close and personal with her that summer. Anyway, considering that Lucy from *TOWIE* had been brought in to select which lines to stock, there was not a lot of choice in Vardo. I'll be honest, I was bored by it, but it does have a good underwear and bikini section, so I went wild.

While we're on boutiques, I do think that Sam and Billie's shop Minnies is gorgeous. Here's the difference – those girls have some serious style. When they had the real launch (not the fake telly one), the queue of girls went on for miles, and the clothes they're pictured out in always sell out in seconds. It's a pretty smart idea to set up shop when you can advertise the clothes in the papers for free. I think my style's really similar to Sam's, so that's probably why I lap up all her outfits.

I had to catch a flight to France on Friday morning from Stansted, then the plan was to be meet Ben at a bar in Nice airport. He'd been at the Grand Prix in Spain the weekend before so he'd extended his stay to make it a week-long holiday. Alright for some. He didn't go to all the Grands Prix as that would just get ridiculous, but he did pretty much do all the European ones. So while I'd been running around like a mad woman, he'd been chilling by a pool. I mean, I'd only just managed to fit in that spray-tan the day before, which killed me. I could still smell it! I'd also let myself down at the bureau de change when I'd asked for francs. The man gave me such a look of pity. Alright, alright, I hadn't been there since the school's French exchange. Why would I keep track of their currency situation?

Dad had offered to drive me to the airport, but when he does this he always pretends he's a taxi driver. He's got an E-type Jag, for fuck's sake. He'll say things like, 'Where you going on your holibobs, darling,' or 'I had that Jackie Fox in my cab the other day. Went without paying.' He even dished out a new dad-gag when he saw me in my mirrored aviators which went, 'Nice sunnies, love. I can really see myself in those.' It was all so painful at 8 a.m., but that's the price you pay for door-to-door service.

'How you getting from Nice to Monaco then?' asked Dad, driving well up the rear of the car in front. I really don't think he's a good enough driver to own a classic car.

'I've got no idea. I was just leaving that to Ben,' I replied.

'You don't want to be relying on a bloke to get you places, love.'

'Well it's done me alright so far since I'm the one off to Monaco and you're not.'

'Yeah, yeah, rub it in. Before you came along, he was meant to be taking me to the Grand Prix.'

'Maybe next year, Dad.'

'I don't think I've got what it takes to be seen on his arm. Talking of which, guess who I've seen on your brother's arm recently.' Dad is *the* biggest gossip I know. He's ten times worse than Mum.

'I haven't got a clue. Brooke?' I wouldn't put it past her.

'Nah. His new Doris is only bloody Sue.'

'Come again? You talking about Sue of Cheryl and Sue?'

'That's the one.'

'Shut the fuck up. You're having me on?'

'Does this look like a face that would mug you off, princess?'

'You're not joking? You're serious?'

'Yep, he's been fitting Sue's new carpets. And that's not all he's been fitting in.'

'This is so gross.'

'Happens all the time when you're working in lonely women's houses. Before I met your mum, I got a lot of action that way. You can learn a lot from an older woman.'

'DAD! Please don't talk any more. I don't even want to know how you know or any of the details. I'm guessing Mum's oblivious.'

'Yeah, course she is. That's why I'm telling you. I've had to hold it in for a whole week. She'd go spare if she knew.'

The world had gone mad. Mum's friend was doing my brother, Brooke was doing my ex and Gemma and Grant were doing everyone but each other. I always think life would be so much simpler if we didn't enjoy sex. It causes a shit-load of grief. I wasn't surprised about Sue because she'll try it on with any man, dead or alive. I mean, Mum actually walked in on Sue going down on their therapist last year. But I never had Jake down for a granny-fiddler. I won't lie, I was disgusted.

When we got to the airport, Dad yanked my baggage out the back and handed me a wodge of euros. 'Look after yourself, Honkytonks, and buy yourself something nice.'

'Dad, you don't have to give me that.'

'Please, you'll make an old man very happy. Plus that's the money I got out after Ben said I'd be going on this romantic break with him.'

I don't think there is a more giving dad than Don Fox. He's been throwing his cash at us a lot more recently. He keeps banging on about not being long for this world. He's pretty melodramatic for a very healthy sixty-year-old with both his parents still alive. I don't actually know how he's made so much money, but if you ask him what he does for a living, he'll tell you he's a professional landlord and investor. All I know is that he's a builder by trade (though I've never seen him graft in my lifetime), he owns the carpet shop Jake works at but he has a manager that does all the work for him, and he has fifty-one properties on his portfolio, most of which have had their mortgage paid off. Pretty impressive, right?

It helps that he's done a lot of cash-in-hand stuff like most people in Essex do. I mean, a lot of the beauty salons round here only accept cash. The taxman can't monitor every pedicure and nor can he monitor how much Dad charges for rent. Essex is like some sort of unofficial tax haven really. We've gone down the same route as Monaco so I reckon just make the county a republic and be done with it. I mean, you can justify anything round here with the phrase, 'It's Essex, innit.' So if you were to say, 'I don't have no cash for my pedicure,' the beautician would say, 'Sorry, darling, it's Essex, innit. There's an ATM five minutes down the road. We'll keep your dog as a hostage.'

We've got our own set of rules round here and it's normal to walk about with wads of cash instead of using your debit card. You'd see what I mean if you got your groceries from Buckhurst Hill Waitrose. Fifties flying everywhere, and before the taxman even gets a snifter, it's spent. It won't surprise you that Dick Turpin came from these parts. Although Dad would say the taxman's the highwayman in this day and age.

The easyJet flight was the only thing I'd forked out for on this trip. Ben and his sponsors were covering everything else, which was a pretty sweet deal. I had to keep reminding myself these shitty two hours on the plane would be the only roughing it I'd be doing. Honest to God, I don't know how Brooke works on these flights. She doesn't come from a monied-up family so she had to find a job fast after university. She lives for holidays abroad so it seemed the obvious option, but whether you're an employee or customer of easyJet, its basically still the airline equivalent to KFC: it does the job but you always feel dirty afterwards. All she wants is a piece of British Airways action. I know that's going to happen for her one day, and then she'll never have to wear orange again. A total tan clasher.

When I got to Nice, I had instructions to meet Ben in the airport's members' bar, the Cap Ferrat Lounge. Sounded fancy. I made my way up there to find Ben and Gino swigging back the beers. It was seriously unfancy for an exclusive lounge. I was expecting chandeliers, big armchairs and offers of neck massages, but it was more like a quiet doctor's waiting room with some colourful chairs. Didn't seem to bother them, though.

'Oh, I see, I see, drinking already, are we?' I said in a pass-agg way that would ensure a drink came my way.

'I'll order you something. Champagne?' said Gino, who'd started letching all over me already. Before I had a chance to reply, Ben had grabbed my face and pulled me in for a full-on snog. It was amazing. It was like we hadn't seen each other for months even though it had only been a week. My champagne radar started beeping so I stuck my arm out for Gino to put the glass in my hand while I carried on snogging Ben. We only stopped because I could feel Gino was getting off on it. He was so gross! Ben was looking even fitter than the last time I'd seen him.

'Hun, you're looking so tanned,' I said, touching his arms. His biceps were practically bursting out of his polo shirt.

'It's been well hot in Spain, babe. Like when I was sunbathing, my belly button would fill up with sweat,' he replied. If anyone else had said this I would have up-chucked, but even this vision of Ben was a turn-on. In fact, I would have sucked that sweat right out of his belly button.

I thought we'd just be getting a taxi from the airport, but no. He'd hired a fucking helicopter. I am serious! Getting a helicopter from Nice to Monaco is one of the most incredible things I've ever done. But word to the wise, don't wear a floaty maxi dress if you're going to do this as it will blow up. Luckily I had my best La Senza thong on and some high espadrilles, so my tanned cheeks would have looked amazing at the heliport.

The ride over the French coast wasn't long enough for my liking, but I got over that once we drew up at Hôtel de Paris. I've stayed in a lot of classy joints, but this beat the lot of them. The suite was probably the same size as my cottage, and to my joy it was wall-to-wall pink with a pink carpet and pink roses on a table. The bathroom was packed with Hermès products which I would be stealing later. There was even a terrace overlooking the sea! That's where I got my first proper bird's-eye view of the racetrack. I had to contain myself. If Brooke had been here we'd have been jumping on the bed hugging and screaming. As it was, I acted cool as you like and opened the champagne that was sat in a bucket of ice.

Whoever says money doesn't make you happy is just telling themselves that to make themselves feel better. Those sad sacks would totally backtrack if they got given a weekend of extravagant luxury with limitless possibilities ahead. I think I sat on the terrace drinking with Ben for about an hour before I could really speak. I forgot to put suncream on so annoyingly I had a red chest for my first night in Monaco. Or is it Monte Carlo? I don't really understand the difference. It's such a small place, just call all of it Monaco and be done with it. And yeah, I get they're not French now but they still speak French, so that's what's confusing.

Now let me share something with you about dirty weekends away because it's something I wish I'd known. I used to have a major phobia of going to the toilet in hotel rooms in case the bloke heard and then that would destroy the myth that women don't do number twos. And on one weekend away eight years ago, I hadn't been the whole time and that obviously puts pressure on your organs. While 69-ing with me on top, the exertion got too much and I ended up guffing in the bloke's face. It was such a passion-killer and I dumped him as soon as we got home because I couldn't ever face him again.

Now what if this had actually been my future husband? Proper BHQ moment.

I told Gemma about my toilet phobia while we were shopping and she said, 'Why don't you just turn on the taps when you go to the toilet?' That was a total news-flash to me. So I said, 'But if I'm running all the taps, won't the bloke know what I'm up to,' and she said, 'It's standard code. Everyone's protected, no questions asked.' Who knew? So I tried it for the first time in this Monaco hotel room with Ben. A bit risky, I know, because he was so hot. But it totally worked! I was in there for a good ten minutes and we had lovely afternoon sex (the best kind, in my opinion) as soon as I came out.

If you learn anything from me, let it be that.

Once a Player, Always a Player

We were going to yet *another* fashion show for our first night on the town. I won't lie, I was sick of fucking fashion shows by this point. But then Ben said there would be loads of F1 racing drivers modelling. The lovely Alonso! That gave the night a bit more edge. I started getting ready at 4 p.m., and by 7.30 p.m. I was ready.

Getting ready with Ben in the room was a huge eye-opener. I thought I'd have the bathroom to myself, but I'd only been in there an hour before he started banging on the door. I've never lived with another bloke apart from my brother, so I don't know how long men take to get ready normally. From what I remember, Charlie spent thirty seconds beautifying himself before a big night out, but I thought back to that drawer in his bathroom and realized Ben would be taking as long as me. So as I was getting ready, I kept one eye on him to see what he was up to.

He spent ages shaving his chest in the shower, for one thing. Then he applied a gradual tanner all over. What's the point of a gradual tanner? But I kept my opinion to myself. Then he shaved his face so precisely that he kept a very even stubble. Then he applied a different self-tan to his face. Turns out he was a real Clarins fan too. Even though he had seriously short hair, he still managed to spend twenty minutes grooming his strands with his gel-covered fingertips. It was hypnotic to watch. Then he put on a bit of foundation, some bronzer, some under-eye concealer, a dab of lip balm and curled his lashes. Plus he spent half an hour selecting his outfit, which ended up being jeans, a tight V-neck top and a black jacket. It's what Mark Wright would call 'The Italian look'. Oh, and he did some press-ups!

I suppose I always say I don't wake up looking like this and it turns out neither did Ben. I couldn't decide if I liked it or not. It annoyed me that Charlie had always been a bit slack with his appearance, although he did love his designer brands. But I was now faced with the other extreme and it was a bit of a surprise. He didn't even comment on my outfit, which was this stunning gold jumpsuit with gold strappy sandals. I wasn't about to beg for a compliment so I gave him a bit of stick about how much he loved himself, and he pulled me in for a kiss. He clearly hadn't picked up my pass-agg tone.

The fashion party turned out to be fucking amazing and blew the previous two right out the water. It took place poolside on the Plaza's rooftop and the party continued at a place called the Amber Lounge. We had a pass that gave us unlimited drinks, so I was well hammered on the sparkling rosé. I don't think it was champagne so it wasn't as flash as it sounds. Kim Kardashian was there, Taio Cruz performed, but no Alonso. I was gutted. There were ten other racing drivers all trussed up in white suits for the show, but they were no lookers. I was pretty confident I'd have to bump into Alonso at some point over the weekend, especially as Ben had met him before. He was my golden ticket.

I tell you who took my breath away, though – that Charlene who's now married Albert of Monaco. Stunning. There were a lot of haters that night calling her Trashlene, but I reckon that's because the girl done good and that makes the ladies well jel they're not her. She hasn't got that great a lifestyle anyway if she's got to have sex with a bald man for the rest of her married days. And when I got back to Essex I read that she tried to escape the country and get out of the wedding. You can't hate someone that unhappy, however minted they are. But anyway, I felt right at home surrounded by all the beautiful people except everyone was too well behaved. No one was jumping up and dancing on the couches like they do in Essex clubs. No one was crying, not even that Charlene. No one was even tempted to push anyone in the pool.

I couldn't really complain, though, and I thought I could definitely get used to the Monaco lifestyle. Even though I was seriously hanging the next morning, it was made slightly more bearable when the one thing on my to-do list was sunbathe on a luxury yacht. The only irritation was the cars whizzing past during the qualifier. At first it was a novelty but eventually I felt every engine rev hit the back of my skull. The yacht belonged to one of Ben's sponsors and this would be the location we'd be watching the Grand Prix from as well so I made a mental note not to drink to excess that night. No way was Monaco going to get the better of me. If I'd had any doubts about Ben initially, they all faded away on deck. I was living this incredible existence because I'd taken a massive gamble on Ben. Perhaps I was starting to feel a bit cocky, but it was while I was soaking up the rays in my bikini that I decided I would get Ben to rub suntan lotion on my back and start a much avoided conversation. Always best to do this when you're practically naked and can't make eye contact. You get more answers.

'Hun, how come you don't introduce me as your girl-friend?' I asked. I could feel the suntan-rubbing get a bit faster. I knew this would be tricky. I waited.

'I've not really thought about it,' Ben said, trying to be proper casual. 'Do you want me to?'

'No, it's fine, but people look like they want to know more when you just say, "This is Becci," then leave it at that. It's a bit strange.'

'None of their business is it, babe? We know what we're about and that's all that matters.'

I wasn't going to leave it at that.

'So don't you want to be my boyfriend?'

'Course I do, babe.'

'Alright then, that's sorted. So are you going to take me out for lunch or what?'

Now see – what I did there was I kept it nice and short because Ben's not the soppy type, but he was so grateful I'd changed the subject, he agreed to a slap-up meal at a three-star Michelin restaurant. Although, I didn't rate the grub there – I've had better meals in Sugar Hut and that's saying something – but there must have been some sort of aphrodisiac in the food because Ben was so hot for me afterwards we ended up having a quickie in the hotel toilets, even though our room was just upstairs. Then he booked me in for a major pampering session in the spa while he went to the casino. So all in all, it was an epic win for me.

The plan for that evening was to go on yet another yacht for a charity dinner, then on to somewhere called the Billionaire Club. That sounded like a place I belonged in. The charity thing was not my scene at all. It was on some boat called *Lady Joy* but there was no joy to be had. The women were told to take off their heels to protect the boat. I'm sorry, but don't have a party on a boat then. No way was I taking my heels off. Some woman had a go at me and when she walked off I heard her friend go, 'People from Essex are hateful anyway, darling.' These people are meant to have manners too! At least in Essex we've got the decency to say these things behind people's backs *and* to their faces.

When I saw that Charlene girl was at the party too, I felt her pain. She was dealing with a ship-load of snobs, so good luck to her, I say. Michael Schumacher showed up wearing some embarrassing leather trousers (something Don Fox would be well jel of). The only excitement on the boat was the buzz for tomorrow's big event. Everyone was chattering about pole positions and bigging up the drivers' parade and saying how amazing all the final-night parties were. Ben was going to take me to the pits where he said he'd find Alonso for me. Result!

The only thing missing from Monaco was my girls. They would have dissed the boring boat, but they'd have gone mad for the Billionaire Club because this was our kind of joint. As we rolled up to the hotel, the sight was incredible. Porsche after Bentley after Ferrari, all waiting for the valets to park their cars. We totally looked the part in the black Rolls-Royce Ben had borrowed off his mate. I'm not joking, the number plate said GOD on it! The club was at the top of the hotel and was run by that short old racing tycoon who went out with Naomi Campbell. Unbelievable who women can bring themselves to do.

I'd got my look bang-on for the occasion with a strapless black sparkly number which left nothing to the imagination as far as my 34Ds were concerned. I now had Ben's full attention. Well, for the first half of the night anyway.

That bloody Gino was there too but I couldn't complain really as he would introduce me to people whenever Ben disappeared. And he'd introduce me as Ben's girlfriend. Ben still hadn't been able to say the word to people, but since we'd got it all out in the open, I was less worried. These things take a while. No matter, I saw Jason Statham that night and it turns out he's an uglier version of Ben. Who knew? Ben was loving that, so I got a picture of the two of them together. I kept my eye out for Alonso but Ben said no drivers would be out the night before the Grand Prix. I said, 'Surely they're just sitting in a car, so they can do that hung-over?' Ben was proper unimpressed with my observation. So unimpressed that I didn't see him for an hour after that. Let him have his tantrum, I thought.

So I got talking to an American guy who just looked rich. Tanned, crisp white clothes and perfect teeth, but I could still tell he was old enough to be my dad. Turned out he was the boss of some NASCAR racing team. I don't know, so don't ask. But the more we talked, the more I realized that he was actually really keen to get Ben over to the States and do trials out there. Being the dutiful 'girlfriend' that I am, I totally bigged up my boyfriend. I'd say the usual sort like, 'Lewis Hamilton is majorly paranoid about Ben entering F1,' and 'Jenson Button's doing everything in his power to stop Ben getting a serious sponsor here.' That's how you do it in Essex, you just spread rumours until enough people believe them. Like, I was telling women at wedding fairs that Denise Van Outen bought her wedding dress from our shop. She hadn't, but since word of mouth is well powerful round our way, the spring of 2009 was nicely profitable. Essex rule: Never let the truth get in the way of a good story. I'm a really good person to have on side, and this Yankee was drinking in every drop of it.

Then he suddenly changed the subject and went, 'Sweetheart, have you ever done TV work?'

My heart beats proper fast when I smell opportunity.

'No, but people keep telling me I should,' I replied, and that's true.

'Well, I agree with them. You've got star quality about you,' he said.

'Oh my God, I've always seen myself in something like 90210 or *Gossip Girl*.'

'Well, I know a lot of producers that could hook you up. You and Ben should come to LA sometime. I've got plenty of room at mine if you need a place to stay.'

'I would love that!' I screamed.

Essex, Monaco, LA . . . what next? I could physically feel life escalating. I mean, that's all it takes to make it big. You just have to meet that one person who can turn things around for you, whether it's professionally or romantically. So far Ben had totally improved my world for the better, but I felt my career was still falling by the wayside. Don't get me wrong, I put a hundred and ten per cent into Tasha's shop, but did I really want to be working for my sister for the rest of my days? However, I couldn't go any further with the conversation because the American's young blonde girlfriend came over to drag him away. A girl can sense when her sugar daddy's up to no good, and she was right. He handed me his card before following her and whispered in my ear, 'By the way, I like your dress. But I like what's underneath it better.'

I was speechless, but I suppose he's only human. I told myself that his parting words were a promising sign because, as we all know, sex sells. By this point, loads of people were up on the white sofas dancing – finally! So I got up there and danced my heart out without any judging eyes. I had to celebrate my networking skills with a victory dance, but I felt less joy without Brooke. Being away from Essex had opened my eyes to a few things, and I decided me and Brooke would have a serious chat when we got back. Her friendship was too important to me and I knew she'd be too proud to make the first move. I hold my hands up – I'd been a total boys' girl; but that's what happens when you start dating, right?

The night got more debauched with women in leather hot pants dancing on podiums, and there was just wall-to-wall beautiful people doing seriously dirty dancing. The highlight for me was the champagne parade through the club where they attached giant sparklers to bottles of Cristal, which lit up the place like Christmas. How a sparkler ended up in my cleavage I'll never know. It's hard to admit this, but this club was Essex in overdrive. I know – whenever I say that, it blows people's minds. I even did a couple of lines with Ben. Like I said, I don't do class As no more, but sometimes I get the devil in me and just want to get totally off my face. So much for curbing excess, but how often to you get to do that in Monaco, right?

By 4 a.m. I was proper gone and realized I needed to go home. Only problem was I'd lost Ben. I worked my way through the whole club and decided there was nothing for it but to check the bloke's toilets. I'm classy, so I didn't go in myself, but this guy was about to so I tried to catch his attention.

'Oi, *monsieur . . . monsieur . . .*' But he didn't respond, so I shouted, '*Oi, mister.*' The word came out of nowhere, but at least he took some notice. He turned to me and went, '*Oui? Parlez français?*'

'*Umm, un petit pois,*' I replied, but instantly regretted it because firstly, I didn't know any French past that, and secondly, he was pissing himself laughing.

'*Je suis desolée*, love, but you know as much French as me,' he replied in an English accent.

'Why did you just answer me in French then?'

'You started it.'

Hmmm, I couldn't argue with that.

'Funny. Anyways, do me a favour. Since you're going in the men's . . .'

'Do you want to come in too?'

'No, no – you going to let me finish? If you see a bloke in there who looks like Freddie Ljungberg, could you tell him his girlfriend's waiting outside.'

Off he went and I hung outside for about five minutes. I thought maybe this bloke had got chatting to Ben or something, but he came out by himself.

'You still here?'

'Errr, yeah. I was waiting for you.'

'That's good of you.'

'And . . . did you see a man who looked like Freddie?'

'Nah.'

'What you been doing in there this whole time then?'

'We've only just met, love. You're a bit personal, aren't you?'

I stormed off. I hate fucking time-wasters and people who think they're funny. I know I've just described my dad there, but he's old. He can't help it. This guy was about thirty and should have known better.

'Oi, oi, oi, where you going to?'

'None of your business,' I replied, but he kept talking at me as I waited for the lift down from the club.

'Look, I'm not being rude,' I said, 'but I've had a really amazing night and I don't want it ruined now. I've lost my boyfriend and now you're just winding me up. So fuck off, will you?' I instantly regretted being such a bitch, but my patience wears thin when I'm drunk and tired.

'I was leaving anyway, Miss Hoity-Toity.'

'Good. Well, let's just stay silent from now on.' To be fair to him, he did shut up. But when I got a taxi outside, he went, 'Where you going?'

'Hôtel de Paris,' I said.

'Me too. Makes sense to share, don't it?'

'I suppose so.'

He tried to make conversation with me on the way back, which turned out to be a well short drive. He was actually an alright person, but he was dressed in cargo shorts and a white T-shirt. He looked more Margate than Monaco. By the time we got to the hotel, I'd warmed to him a bit. Turns out he was a musician, and, as you know, I can't help respect someone who's got a gift.

'This has been one of the most rollercoaster twenty minutes of my life,' he said as he paid the taxi guy.

'I'll take that as a compliment,' I said. 'Good job I met you cos I actually had no cash for a cab.'

'So you AND the Queen don't carry money around? You must be from a very elite background,' he said.

'Yeah, I am. West Essex.'

He paused, then pissed himself laughing. Oh, charming.

'That would explain why you're staying at the Hôtel de Paris.'

'Yeah, but so are you.'

'Nah, I'm not.'

'But you said . . .'

'I was enjoying the ride so much I didn't want to get off, did I?'

'Oh my God, you're such a freak.'

'I just enjoy a woman with a bit of spirit. What's the crime?'

'Whatever. Listen, I'm off, so you toddle back to whatever shithole you're staying at and let's get on with our lives.'

'Oooh, hangbags,' he said, doing a camp gesture at me. 'Listen, what's your name, anyway?'

'I don't give out personal information, babe.'

'No matter, I have ways of finding these things out. See ya,' and he walked off all breezy and whistling. Wasn't that such a creepy way to end a conversation? But I didn't have time to give that bloke a second thought cos I needed to get into my hotel room somehow.

Since I didn't have a key to the room, I took off my

shoes and banged hard and loud with the heel. Nothing. So I went all the way back down to the hotel lobby and got the spare key to the room and up I went again. I opened the door and surprisingly all the lights were on. Ben's clothes were scattered on the floor in the hall and hanging off the sofa.

I followed the trail of clothes into the bedroom and saw the most predictable sight. A blonde bouncing up and down on Ben's cock.

Oh no, not just any old blonde. The blonde girlfriend of that American guy. And it gets worse. Guess who's filming it all? Well, I couldn't see who it was until I heard Ben go, 'Now go suck Gino off.'

'*What the fuck's going on?*' I yelled. Everyone turned to look at me but they didn't look very shocked or worried. 'Well, is someone going to give me some answers?'

Gino calmly got up from his chair and tried to escort me away from the scene of the crime. 'Put some pants on, would you?' I said all wildly as I shook him off me. I didn't want his saggy man-tits anywhere near me. I had to keep my eyes on the ceiling to avoid looking at his old boy which was now properly standing to attention. He had the worst kind too: fat and short. I was scarred for life.

Ben and the blonde were perfectly still and just staring at me. Gino duly found his pants and I stormed back into the living room before he had a chance to touch me again.

'I don't understand. Why's everyone acting like *I'm* the mental, like I've walked into a perfectly normal scene?'

'We thought you knew about this. We thought that's why you hadn't come back.'

'Why the fuck would I know about this? Did you text me about it at some point in the night to go, "Ben's banging someone else tonight so if you could make yourself scarce, that'd be well nice of you." Fuck you, Gino.'

'When you'd vanished, we assumed Mike had found you.'

'Who the hell's Mike?' I asked, suddenly confused.

'The American guy. Sylvie's boyfriend,' said Gino.

'Is that Sylvie in there?' I said through gritted teeth.

'Correct.'

'And Mike's the old guy?'

'Correct.'

'*So why's Ben banging his girlfriend?*' I yelled.

'Because Mike's meant to be banging you.'

My blood ran cold. The situation hit me like a massive wave and I fell back onto the sofa and just muttered, 'He's swopped me.'

'Not really. It's more like Mike did the swopping and Ben agreed,' chirped Gino.

'Oh, that's alright then,' I said, getting some fire in me. 'Fine, you want to play this game. Tell me what room Mike's in.'

'Why don't you join our party?' said Gino casually.

'Room number, please.'

'323, across the hall,' he replied reluctantly.

I grabbed my bag and slammed the door behind me. I didn't really know what I was doing. I did know I was furious and I wanted revenge. So I banged on room 323 but the door was already open. I walked into this Mike's room and found him butt-naked except for his white socks. Thankfully, he was asleep, but face down on the bed in this horrible star-shape position that left nothing to the imagination. What a fucking weird situation. My need for revenge had subsided with this vision and my survival instincts kicked in. I spotted Mike's wallet on the side of his bed and took out every note in there. It was technically looting, but I was owed.

I sat on the sofa and got on my iPhone to book the first easyJet flight out of there. Since no one in their right mind was flying out of Nice on Grand Prix day, that part was easy. I had less than five hours until my flight took off so there was no hurry. I just lay on the sofa for another hour drifting in and out of nightmares before pulling myself together. I was still pretty out of it, so I went back down to the lobby at 7 a.m. and did an espresso shot while the hotel called me a taxi.

There I was, sat in the back of a French cab in last night's outfit and my clutch stuffed with euros. That's when the sadness set in. And I mean the sort of sadness that squeezes your heart so hard you feel actual physical pain. At first it was silent sobbing where your mouth's open but only hot air and hot tears come out. Then I let out this cry that came from so deep within, it sounded like a wild animal. The taxi driver swerved with shock, which is not good when you're going round the same bends Grace Kelly drove off. Although I'd actually have been thankful to BHQ for putting me out of my misery even if I did die at an all-time low. The thing is, I'm not a crier. I'm not cold or anything, but I don't cry at films, books or get set off by friends crying. The only time I can't cope is if I lose someone. I suppose that's grief. Weirdly, this was the deepest grief I'd ever experienced. I felt more exposed and vulnerable than ever. Once the floodgates were open, they would not shut.

The taxi driver kept trying to speak to me in limited English the whole forty-five-minute journey, but I just waved him away each time he turned around. How the mighty fall . . . arriving in a helicopter of happiness and leaving in a taxi of torment. When we got to the airport, I just shoved all the notes in the guy's hand and walked off. I couldn't talk to the lady at check-in, so I gave her my phone with the booking on. When she asked about baggage, I just showed her my empty hands and cried harder. I think she just wanted to get me away, so no questions were asked.

I spent the next hour walking through duty-free, crying as I spritzed myself with Gucci. We finally started boarding and miraculously the crying turned into whimpering. But once I stepped on board and saw all those attendants in their neon orange uniforms, I started bawling again. Not just because it's such a nasty colour to put anyone in, but I really wanted Brooke to be on the flight, and she wasn't. As I sat sobbing, I knew I needed a friend to meet me at Stansted or I was done for, so I sent a text before the bitchy flight attendant had a go at me for not turning my phone off. Like I could bring down the fucking flight or something. My only luck was that my entire row was empty, so once we'd taken off, I just curled up and kept it to a low moan for the entire two-hour flight.

So there I was, dressed up for a night out, make-up smeared all over my face and tottering in my patent black Louboutins through Stansted. I must have been the best-dressed mess of a person to ever come through arrivals. Surprisingly, someone managed to recognize me. My gorgeous Ryan was there to rescue me and he was clutching a bouquet of flowers. That image still makes my heart melt. We ran to each other like long-lost lovers and he just held me until I'd calmed down again. I was so relieved to be home, but so haunted by the past eight hours.

We walked out the airport hand in hand and then Ryan turned to me and went:

'Babe, we're so going to fix you. Lucky for you, I've got wet wipes in the car to sort your face out. Then we'll sort your heart. We're all here for you, yeah?'

I just nodded and clutched his arm to say thank you, but we didn't say anything else for the rest of the journey home. I felt like such a plum. I don't know why I'd fallen so hard for Ben, but somehow he'd lured me in and then dropped me from the highest point possible.

10

Poor Me, Poor Me, Pour Me Another Drink

I didn't want to talk about Monaco-gate with anyone for the first few days. Mum came over to see if I wanted to go shopping, Dad came over to see if I was coming over for a barbecue, Tasha came round with my niece, Jake didn't come over at all. I just wanted to lock myself away, cuddle up with my little furball Marilyn, watch old *Sex and the City* episodes and feel very sorry for myself. But then I got proper bored. So I finally got back to Gemma, who wouldn't stop leaving voice messages, and I agreed to go out for lunch with her and Ryan at the King Will.

As I made my way to Chigwell, I thought, who knew it was possible to feel so sad driving a Mercedes SLR. If I'm to be honest, I'd really only got sucked into buying it because Ben had one. I majorly missed the Audi TT.

It was so reassuring to see my friends waving me over from the patio with a bottle of rosé on the go. Gemma told me she'd met up with Grant to talk things through, but she didn't feel she could trust him any more. And Ryan told me how he'd been cruising at Virgin Active that morning and a man had jizzed on him in the shower as he watched. So gross, but who knew cruising happened in our gym and so early on? It makes my women's changing room stories look a bit tame.

I could see they were gagging to know what had happened to me in Monaco, so I relayed the whole depraved tale but made sure I kept the descriptions of the luxury and the bling in. I didn't want them to think I was a complete sad sack.

'So has he tried contacting you?' asked Gemma.

'Not once,' I replied.

'He's a fucking arsehole, yeah?' said Ryan.

'I expect he's too ashamed,' Gemma added.

'I don't think Ben knows the meaning of shame. If anything, he's probably bewildered as to why I left, but he's not the sort to chase after a girl once the hunt is over,' I said. And it had been a complete game to him.

'I suppose you weren't official boyfriend and girl-friend, no?' said Ryan.

I grudgingly shook my head in agreement. I couldn't bring myself to mention the conversation I'd had with Ben on the yacht. Looking back, I know he was just after a peaceful life. He'd agreed to be my boyfriend, but he'd never agreed I was his girlfriend. In Ben's world, apparently it's possible to be one without the other. It's almost like I didn't have the right to be devastated, and that just made it all the more devastating.

We worked our way through three bottles of rosé, which is not bad going for a Thursday afternoon. It felt good to be outdoors and eating my first proper meal in days, but I still felt really shaken up. And the anger was starting to rise with all the alcohol. I tell you what still really pisses me off the most about all this: I bloody missed the Grand Prix because of Ben and I never got to meet Alonso and I never went to the amazing post-Grand Prix parties. BHQ had thrown me about until I was black and blue, but where was Ben's comeuppance?

I was in the middle of a proper old rant when I saw a real sight for sore eyes. Looking absolutely stunning in a bright blue playsuit and striped wedges, Brooke came over to our table and gave me a massive hug, which just made me cry again. When would it stop?

'Hun, I'm going to chop his balls off,' said Brooke loud enough for every table to hear.

'He'd have to grow a pair first,' added Ryan. The pair of them cackled and Brooke planted a kiss on his cheek.

'Well, I've got lots of other options. Like I'm going to go around Repton Park and knock on everyone's doors and tell them about the orgies and drugs that are going on in his place. We'll get him evicted like we did Jack Tweed.'

I love it when Brooke talks mean.

'I'm so relieved you're here,' I said, so genuinely. We

looked at each other and just acknowledged we were alright with each other.

'Do I get a glass of rosé or what?' said Brooke, ending the moment. She doesn't really do heart-to-hearts.

When I got home, Mum came running out. 'Ben's been over,' she said, all flustered.

'What you talking about?'

'He dropped your suitcase over and some flowers,' she said, looking expectantly at me as if I was going to break out into a smile.

I ran into the house and saw it all there in the hallway. I picked up the flowers with my suitcase, which I dragged over the gravel to my front door. I then placed the flowers in the middle of the drive and stamped the shit out of them. Mum looked at me like I'd finally lost it. All she could say was, 'Umm, I'm going to revamp the hall. Do you want to help with colour schemes?'

'No, I'm busy,' I said, slamming my front door.

I felt bad, though, because she was only trying to help, and normally I love her yearly hall redecoration. Not many mums have the vision to transform their entrance that regularly, but that's Jackie for you. I'd had loads of Monaco-themed interior ideas while I'd been out there, but all my creativity had been zapped. Although, the chaise longue I'd put in Tasha's shop was just begging to be in Mum's hallway, so I texted her.

After that, it was shutters down in the cottage again with a very frustrated Marilyn.

11

Finding Your Inner Show Pony

Birthdays are a big deal round our way, whatever age you're hitting. Me and the girls call it 'Show Pony Time' because we will go above and beyond when it comes to making ourselves stand out at birthdays. Everyone's made the effort to turn out for you, so the least you can do is make the ultimate effort and give them something amazing to look at.

Sadly for me, my twenty-seventh birthday occurred in June. It was no big shock as it's always then, but I had to get my Show Pony on two weeks after Monaco. I normally embrace getting older and wiser, but when you've just been treated like a whore by the guy you thought was your boyfriend, the future looks bleak. Gemma and Brooke were having none of it, though. As is birthday tradition, Faces nightclub was the destination.

We've been going down there since we were fifteen. Technically that's underage, but if you're a girl with a

good set of boobs, a tight dress and a fake ID, then anything's possible in Essex clubworld. I mean, I wouldn't
know how easy it is to get in illegally these days, but
with free entry for girls before 10 p.m, it's fair to say
we're enticed. Last time we'd been down there, Mark
Wright had shown up and women were literally throwing themselves at him and his car. I wouldn't be
surprised if he'd got home to find a blonde stuck to the
bonnet. I hadn't seen anything like it in all my days.

So Gemma, bless her, had reserved a table at Faces
for this champagne party. We're all members so we'd
have got this anyway, but Gem's step-brother used his
contacts to get us in the VIP pod. The thing is, they say
the roped off 'booths' are VIP, but they're so not. It's all
about the Pod, aka the Cage, as featured in the *TOWIE*
trailer for series two. This white birdcage is situated in
the middle of the club, and you have to go up on the
small stage to get to it. It's one of the hardest VIP areas
to slip into since the narrow entrance is taken up by the
hulking body of one doorman. It's good for the celebs as
they're nicely cossetted in there, and if they're performing, they just slip from Cage to stage and do their thing
without getting near the public. All I've ever wanted is
to book the Cage, and now Gemma had gone ahead and
done it for me. I couldn't really let her down, so I reluctantly dragged myself in for a much needed sunbed and
spray down Beaus & Belles. I was so embarrassed by my
whiteness, but the girls gave me major pity when I told

them how I'd been messed about. I got the usual WEG response: 'Fucking arsehole. You can do better than a cheating shit like that, babe.' Thing is, he hadn't really cheated, had he?

Then I got my gels done and had a major slag-off about girls from *TOWIE*. They had nothing good to say about Lauren Goodger: 'She used to come in here until we started charging her. I mean, who does she think she is? I don't like the girl. She thinks she's stunning, but she's really not.' Maria Fowler on the other hand – they're all over her. Since she went out with the manager of Nu Bar, people can't get enough of the 'extra' round here. Probably because Maria has to work a bit harder for it and almost got chucked out of it after all those escort stories emerged. So she's keeping it real, whereas Lauren thinks she owns the show. Well delusional.

I felt a bit more like myself after my MOT and I felt empowered to give something back to the world, so I took Marilyn down the doggy spa. He needed all my salty tears washed out of his coat and his chest-beard reshaped. Luckily Marilyn's pretty cheap to run, but if you've got a Russian Black Terrier, you're looking at twice the price. I got him the full grooming works with salon treatments, which included a bubble bath, a fresh facial scrub, a nail and paw treatment, an intense conditioning treatment for his coat and a spritz of aromatherapy cologne to help him chill out. While I was there, I got his stinky breath sorted and his nails painted silver. He looked stunning. His proud fluffy face proper lifted me. I hadn't thought about Ben once that morning. Don't I always say it, treating yourself and others is essential for your mental well-being. I don't get why women would feel guilty for looking after themselves when it's really for the benefit of everyone?

I'd eagerly promised Tasha I'd look after the shop that afternoon as I wanted to keep busy, but it was so bleeding quiet that I just sat staring into space going over everything. It was doing my head right in because I hadn't had the chance to have it out with Ben. My main fear in all this was that I'd become as naïve as Cheryl and Sue. I honestly have amazing instincts when it comes to players, and sometimes I'm on the same page as them. I always know what I'm getting myself into and I thought I had been guarded that first time Ben got his 'man' to acquire me in One9Five, but I'd never been chased/stalked to that extent before and then we'd got so intimate. I didn't mention he'd got me a matching gold Cartier watch, did I? I thought I was well in there, but I was just being groomed for his sick agenda. It's that age-old mistake women make, though, isn't it? I thought going out with me was changing him and that I'd bagged myself a well nice lifestyle too.

I'll let you into a secret and this is true. There's this really small window of opportunity where a player decides he wants to get married, and whoever he's going out with at the time, that's the chosen woman. It's pure chance. I thought that woman was me, if I'm totally honest. You live and learn, right? The only bonus from all this was I'd lost half a stone, so I was looking skinny as you like. Who needs to Shit Yourself Thin when you've got heartache and humiliation? I was totally going to make the most of my new flat stomach at Faces. It was Show Pony Time.

Since we weren't getting ready together, I had to put the calls in to see what everyone else was wearing. Or more like, I told them I was wearing black and suggested we'd all look the business if they did too. You cannot go wrong with a Forever Unique dress. It set me back £360, but it's only your birthday once a year and I'd worked hard enough for it. It was black, clingy and ruched with these stunning silver-jewelled and beaded shoulders. Normally I'm not a big fan of my bum, but the dress held the curves in all the right places and the draped neckline made my boobs look like they were on an escape mission. I felt amazing and ready to make my entrance.

As usual, I was still doing my hair when I heard the honk outside in the driveway. When I finally opened the door, there were Brooke, Gemma and Ryan standing by a white limo waving a bottle of pink Laurent Perrier and four flutes!

'Oh my God, you guys!' I said, struggling over the gravel in my Jimmy Choos. 'How the fuck did you keep all this secret from me?'

'It was the most difficult thing I've had to hold in for twenty-four hours,' said Gemma, 'but since we're not doing the limo for my hen do, then we might as well do it now.'

Ryan thrust a cold glass of fizz in my hand and Gemma yelled, 'Here's to us lucky bitches . . . still got it,' as we raised our glasses. We looked the nuts, all dressed in black like we were going to a movie premiere.

'Thanks for making my birthday proper special,' I said, welling up a bit. 'I've spent a lot of time eating Haribo under a blanket with Marilyn, so thank you for getting me out. I love you all.'

'If you don't pull tonight, you will have let us down though, yeah?' said Ryan.

'We are looking so fly tonight, I don't see how I couldn't,' I said, trying to convince myself.

'C'mon Show Pony, trot on into your limo, yeah?' said Ryan, slapping my butt as I did so. I always say Ryan puts on this big gay act so he can slap our bums and grab our boobs without us pressing charges. It would be a totally Essex-man thing to do.

The ride to Gants Hill was twenty minutes of hysteria. We gave up on the glasses cos they kept spilling everywhere, so we just swigged out of the bottle and sang Lady Gaga at the top of our voices. A bit of 'Bad Romance' seemed so fitting. Ryan kept wanting us to stick our heads out the window, but he didn't really get how long we'd spent on our hair. Alright for him – he puts so much gel in his hair, it's like lead.

I still get the adrenalin rush when I walk down the black hall and open those double doors to Faces. Or 'Faeces' as it's known by those too intimidated to return. You never forget your first club experience, and it blew my tiny mind back in the day. I'd never seen anything like it: the energy, the clothes, the stares. I loved it before it even got the makeover. As we made our way to the Cage, I squealed at the sight of those zebra-print sofas and champagne laid out for us on the glossy monochrome tables. It was a step up from the days of drinking WKD with a straw to get off my face faster. Now I drink Bollinger with a straw.

With my eye on the prize, I made my way up before a huge arm landed in front of me.

'Can't go in there. Private party,' said the bouncer.

'Uh, yer, I know. It's my party.'

'No it ain't.'

'What do you mean?'

'A celebrity's hired this out and it ain't you.'

The bouncers in Faces are well off. We all started screeching and then Gem came skidding over.

'Shit, we've been shoved,' she said. 'I only got this on the condition someone more important didn't hire it and they have. So we've got a VIP booth now.'

'That's bang out of order,' I said. 'Why can't we share?'

'Don't matter, they've just given me another bottle of champagne on the house,' said Gem. 'Honest, my step-brother's known the manager for years and he's alright.'

As Gem dragged me off, I turned to the bouncer and went, 'I'll be back.' He looked nonplussed. I like a mission on a night out and I was getting back in that Cage.

I actually don't know why celebrities come to Faces. Fine if they're being paid to do a personal appearance, but if they come of their own free will, they always get grief. Or dish out grief. And it's always the footballers. Anton Ferdinand got done for punching someone outside who was supposedly mugging him for his watch, Ashley Cole did get mugged for his watch, Manuel da Costa got fined for slapping a woman, most of the Spurs team got kicked out of here after winning some cup. I could go on. And celebrities get verbally abused by drunk clubbers, especially that Danielle Lloyd, but the *TOWIE* lot mostly seem to get respect and awe. Although the beating Sam Faiers got from that girl gang in Chigwell was a bit of a wake-up call. Sam blamed it on 'jealousy', but if you ask me it was the ultimate happy-slap. Imagine those rough-arse girls seeing the result of their nasty work on *TOWIE*? I'm glad they didn't make it a proper storyline, as that's what the perpetrators wanted. Amy Childs went and got herself some security after that and I hope the other girls follow.

Anyways, what I'm saying is celebrities need to be on their guard when they go to clubs in Essex because the locals can sometimes turn. There's something about Faces that makes tensions run particularly high. That's why it's such a legendary institution: it looks classy and sexy on the outside, but it's pure filth and drama deep down. That is West Essex.

If they've not got a champagne night on in Faces, then it's a themed night because we bloody love dressing up around here. So there's the Marbs, Ibiza and Zante Send-off Party, the Beach Party (sexy swimwear gets you in for free), the Essex Models Party (girls told to look their best for model spotters), or my personal favourite, the PJ party where the girls come dressed in silk camis and suspenders while the blokes just wear their normal clothes and flex their muscles. I would say the overall theme for clubbers, mainly girls, is wearing as little clothing as possible.

I don't see why Faces should be called a meat-market if you've got all these stunning women and all these gawping men. I mean, the blokes have to work hard to get our attention, and we're just knocking them right back if they don't have what it takes. The cows can't do that in an actual meat-market can they? So the bottom line is, the ladies got the power and the ladies get in for free. What's not to like?

Did I mention the podiums? Brooke's actually taken pole-dancing classes, and she's proper amazing. I ordered her to give me a personal show and she did not disappoint. She climbed onto that podium, grabbed the pole with the confidence of a pro and started flicking her black hair while her body was spinning and her legs were swinging. Within one minute, she'd built up a serious audience of admirers, probably hoping she'd flash her vajazzle. She made me try it once, but I just ended up getting pole burns between my thighs. I think I went too fast down it.

I spotted my brother walking in with all his mates, so I waved him over.

'Happy birthday, babe,' he said.

'Thanks, hun. Where's my present?'

'Alright, alright, calm the passion. It's on its way.'

'You say that every year,' I said.

'Whatevs. You want a drink?'

'Yeah, always. First off, talk me through your mates.'

'You know Dave and Jon.' I did. I wasn't impressed. 'And this is Jamie.' Proper fit.

'Alright, James,' I said, winking at him for some reason. But it's OK, he wasn't put off.

'May I say you're looking very gorgeous tonight,' replied Jamie. 'If I'd known you were his sister, I'd have been round his gaff much sooner.'

'I've actually got my own place next door. You should come check it out.'

'Oi, oi, oi, stop flirting with my mate,' Jake butted in.

'I don't know what you're talking about. Where's

this drink you promised me?' Jake went off, dissing me with all his mates in tow. Charming. Ryan immediately sidled up to me.

'I totally thought that was Ryan Gosling, but then I was like, what's he doing in Faces?' he babbled. 'Like there's room for two Ryans here. I gotta say, I like a man with a strong chin. And those sexy eyes are nice, yeah? Why's Jake not shown us *him* before?'

'Oh my God, are we attracted to the same man for once?'

'Yeah, I think two can play that game. We found our first love slave,' he said, still checking Jamie out as he walked to the bar. 'I tell you what, though. I'm going to totally let you have him all to yourself just because you need a good seeing-to,' said Ryan, cupping my face.

'Awwww, that's so sweet of you, babe.'

'You're welcome. And I'll do your brother, yeah?' said Ryan as he kissed me on the lips. I've told him not to do that. What if people think he's my boyfriend and they're all put off? He's always trying to hold my hand in bars and clubs too. Nightmare.

By 11 p.m. it was heaving in there, and while I'd taken my eye off the Cage with all the drinking and dancing I'd been doing, it was now suddenly occupied. I went over to take a closer look and clocked the VIP thief. A bloody footballer. Do they not know any other clubs round here? It was so empty in there too! I grabbed Gemma and Brooke and left the boys to guard our drinks. The bouncer sensed danger, but there was nothing he could do to stop us. I was already waving really vigorously so my boobs jiggled in the footballer's direction. His eyes were practically on stalks. Our entrance was secured.

He came over and went, 'Alright, love?'

'Yeah, yeah, fine, thanks,' I said, looking up at him. 'I just wanted to say that we got kicked out of here earlier because you'd booked it. But the thing is it's my birthday, so it's been a bit shit.'

'You're joking? Well you girls have got to get yourselves back in here then,' he said, and then he turned to the bouncer and went, 'It's alright, they're with me.' As we walked in, I shouted to the heavy, 'Unlucky, hun.' He just shook his head in despair.

Once we had access to the Cage, we got everyone else in too. Got to stagger it or people get suspicious. There was one close miss when a mate of the footballer's stood on Jake's foot and they started squaring up to each other. If something like that happens, Jake never wants a fight, he simply wants the other bloke to apologize. He's got such high standards when it comes to manners and respect. So they stand there for a while with their faces inches away from each other, and Gem's squawking about us getting kicked out. And then suddenly they're shaking hands and giving each other a big old man-hug.

I so wasn't worried because I've seen him do this

time and time again. Jake's a lover, not a fighter, but one day I swear it's not going to work out for him. About five years ago, we had a close encounter while we were waiting for a cab near Nu Bar. A bloke walked past and called me an ugly cunt because I'd told him to bog off earlier that night. So Jake starts squaring up to this guy in that same way. I'm telling him to leave it, but he's not giving up until I get an apology. Then this guy whips out a knife. I'm not kidding you.

Jake turns to me and goes, 'Get my phone out your bag,' and I say, 'What you going to do, call for back-up?'

'Nah, I'm calling Mum,' he replies.

He was actually serious. It was so random that the bloke pissed himself laughing and said something about respecting a man who loves his mum. So I then got my apology and Jake opened his arms for the customary hug. Mum screeched up in the BMW within ten minutes and the bloke waved us off, knife still in hand.

After the commotion, I spotted Jamie and Gemma talking and him taking down her number. What the fuck, I thought. I suppose I hadn't given him any attention since quite a few people had shown up to my do, and I couldn't be neglecting my friends. Still, I didn't like this single Gemma. I found Russ and Rob, who had turned up drunk, and told them to go talk to her. They totally obliged and I made a beeline for Jamie.

'Alright, you having a nice night?' I said.

'Yeah, it's alright in here, isn't it? I thought it'd be a

bit claustrophobic, but now I'm here, I feel like I've gone up in the world. I could get used to your elite ways.'

'That's what I always say about VIP too!' I squealed, even though it was a really shit 'me too' comment.

'You don't remember me at all, do you?' he said suddenly.

'Oh my God, I'm so sorry, have we met before?' I said, racking my brains. 'Was it at one of Jake's filthy white-collar boxing matches?'

'Nah. Think again, love.'

'Do you work with him?'

'Sort of. I can't believe you don't recognize me even a *petit pois*,' he said, smiling.

'What you talking about?'

'I'm the bloke that pissed you off at the Billionaire Club and in the cab. Told you we'd meet again.'

It was a major light-bulb moment.

'You're joking? But you didn't look fit then,' I said. I don't know why, but Jamie had brought the rude side out of me before and it was happening again.

'Oh, ta very much. So I looked minging to you in Monaco?' he asked.

'To be honest, I was drunk, and when people wear bad threads I get face blindness. I remember them horrible shorts,' I said.

'Since I'm dressed a little better tonight, I'll give you that. But I was hoping I'd made *some* sort of impression on you.'

He was actually looking hurt! I was saved from having to answer by Russ, who was dancing with a tray of shots in my face singing, 'Go shawty, it's your birthday, we gonna party like it's your birthday . . .'

'Nah, I'm alright, babe,' I said, trying to brush him away.

Russ stopped singing. 'Drink it,' he said, picking up a shot and pressing it to my mouth. Two After Shocks later, Jamie's appearance made even less sense.

'Are you not really blown away by the coincidence? I mean, I can't get my head around this,' I said once I'd got rid of Russ.

'All it is, I know Jake from travelling in Thailand. Jake invited me out for a big Essex night. I've never been here before, so I thought I'd see what all the hype's about. Oh, and you may have popped up on my Facebook as "someone I might know". In fact that did happen, so that is a bit of a lucky coincidence,' he said, realizing he'd given away far too much information. I sometimes think Facebook is a bit bossy and meddling, but in this instance I was glad I'd been given a second chance with this guy. We could start again and I would be perfectly civil.

'So if you're not from Monaco, where you from?'

'Hackney,' he replied. I'm sorry, but I couldn't hide my disgust. 'You not feeling it?' he asked.

'No offence, but I just can't imagine living there. It looks well depressing. Just saying.'

He made a face that suggested he wanted to rip the piss out of me and I suddenly had a flashback to him calling me Miss Hoity-Toity. I really am.

'Each to their own, I suppose,' he replied, smirking. 'I reckon I could show you a few things round Hackney that would totally change your mind.' He'd now put his arm round my shoulder as he waxed on about this bar and that. It was pure textbook flirting.

'Sorry, hun, but Hackney isn't a patch on Essex. They got clubs like this there?' I asked, actually willing him to mock me.

'We wish – now I've seen the light, I don't know how I'm gonna face clubbing in Hackney again,' he replied. 'But you gotta at least give me a chance to win you over. One night in East London with me, Miss Fox, and you'll never want to leave.'

I pretended to deliberate, he pleaded and eventually I gave him my digits. It was my genuine number too. Sorry to say, I fake-number people about fifty per cent of the time. There's blokes asking every weekend for it, so if I gave them the real deal, about a thousand men would have my number by now. I suppose that means five hundred men actually do have my number. That's proper high, now I think about it. Anyways, after he took my number I was about to get a whole lot more flirty with him, but I was stopped in my tracks. There was Gem looking over at me, all emotional. It didn't look good since he'd been taking hers only ten minutes ago. I made my excuses and went over to her.

'Just like it always used to be,' she said with her eyes all welled up.

'What you talking about?'

'It's just like at school. Blokes humouring me but what they really want is you. And right in my face too.'

'That's not true, Gem. You're being oversensitive.'

'I got eyes, you know.'

'Yeah, but he wasn't taking my number. He was taking the shop's number. His sister's getting married and I told him we'd cut him a deal.'

'You lying?

'I swear on my nan's life I'm telling the truth.' Well, Nan wouldn't mind me using her name to spare Gem's pain. She was right, it was bang out of order to go straight in there after her. Though I got to say, she'd been well touchy since being single. Flying solo didn't suit her.

I wish I could say the rest of the night was as memorable, but it just descended into pure messiness. I will fess up now, I snogged the footballer's mate, who turned out to play for Cardiff City. I'm ashamed to say that I clocked a tan line where his wedding ring had been and I carried on snogging him. I know it's wrong, but I did say no when he asked to come back to mine. So you see, I have limits, and I'd only pulled him so Gemma had a clear run at Jamie (I didn't know I was doing that at the time but that would have been my intention). I didn't realize that Jake's mates had all gone, so it was left to muggins to get him home. They didn't even say good-bye, which was rude. It did flash through my mind that maybe Jamie was disappointed by my naughtiness, but then again, we'd only flirted and I can't control who tries it on. If you don't like it, jog on.

When the cab dropped us off home, I was adamant I was going to sleep in my old bedroom instead of the cottage. Jake was bored of me so he didn't bother argu-ing. But as I got up to the landing, I just felt this wave of nausea and I projectile-vomited red sick right outside Don and Jackie's bedroom. It even hit the wall.

'Ummmmmmmm, they're going to be well pissed off,' whispered Jake like we were kids again.

'Shit,' I slurred. 'I can see the After Shocks.'

But then Jake did the nicest thing he's ever done in our entire lives. He shoved me in my bed and then cleaned up after me. The ultimate display of brotherly love! I owed him big time because he'd done it proper quietly and you couldn't see anything the next day. If Don had found out, he'd have moaned about me ruining his carpets again. He needs to change the record.

12

Polo is for Posing, Not Playing

Gemma and Grant clearly weren't through. She would have contacted everyone to call off the wedding if that was the case. So like the good friend I am, I decided I would take matters into my own hands. We'd all got tickets to the highlight on everyone's calendar, the Duke of Essex Polo at Gaynes Park near Epping, so I texted Grant to say we were all going and to make sure he got himself down there too. I mean, this was the event where Lydia first met Arg. If they could get it on there, then so could Gem and Grant.

I didn't know anyone who *wasn't* going, that's how big a deal it is. Even Mum and Dad were going. I can only explain it as like being at an amazing wedding, but because there's no bride to upstage, you can really go for it. I spent weeks finding the perfect outfit because in the back of my mind I was thinking I'd find romance there too. Anyone who is part of the Essex elite would be there. The polo was on in early July so that would be six weeks and no word from Ben. The longer it went on, the more bitter I got, and that's just not my style. I was going to make the polo my big comeback and I needed the dress to go with it.

I'd been properly blown away by a stunning nude and grey Julien Macdonald dress that I'd seen Cheryl Cole wear. It was as sheer as lingerie, and even though the dress was short, it had this dramatic silk train flowing behind it. Sexy *and* dramatic! It just so happens I know someone who knows Lily, Cheryl Cole's PA (yeah, of course Cheryl has a good, honest Essex girl to guard her deepest secrets), so I got them to contact Lily about it. The information we got back was disappointing. Turns out Julien had made it specially for her and it cost £25,000 and borrowing wasn't an option. But you know you have to own a dress when a year on you're still thinking about it. Well, that dress totally walked into my life without me even trying. I'd managed to beat Tasha down to let me go to this wholesaler – even though I'm the 'buyer' this is the main source of our fights when it comes to the business because, essentially, it's shopping – and there, staring back at me, was an exact replica of the Cheryl dress. So yes, my dress was actually a wedding dress, but who's to know that? And it was free. As long as I didn't get it messy, it was going right back on the shop floor. I was just doing what I do at wedding fairs and modelling the dress, so I was doing Tasha a favour really.

You've got to be well prepared with your beauty treatments the week before the polo. Remember, every Essex woman is treating this like it's her big day, so you got to book your salon appointments before the rest of them face-aches do. I wanted really massive hair for it, so I asked for way more extensions than my usual. When I got home, Mum said I looked like an American. A bit like Pamela Anderson. My hair colour is way nicer, but I took that as a compliment.

Obviously I'd upped my sunbeds to three a week, thinking I wouldn't need fake tan, but I decided two days before that I wasn't brown enough for my liking, so Brooke had to come over and do me in the tent. Naturally I repaid the favour and did her too. Although we had a proper barney because she sprayed tanner in my hair. We couldn't actually see anything, but I told her you couldn't be so cack-handed with blondes and she stormed out the cottage. I was only half-done, so I had to run out in a towel and beg her not to drive off. I have zero dignity.

So as you can see, tensions and hormones were raging. But because of all the preparation, I was pretty together on the big day. I was still the last one into the people carrier, but I was a lot less late than usual.

All the Foxes were there except for Jake, who would be rolling in for the evening debauchery. Tasha and Tony had left my niece Lola with Nan, which meant they were going to get absolutely plastered. And of course, Brooke, the honorary Fox, was riding in style with us.

'Your tits look incredible, babe,' was the first thing Brooke said as I got in.

'Awww, thanks, hun. You look stunning too,' I said. 'But can I just say, one of us is going to fall out of their dress at some point today. So we keep an eye out for any escapees, yeah?'

'I wouldn't mind being a warden at that prison,' Tony piped up from the front.

'Give it a rest, Tone, and stop earwigging,' I shouted back.

I sometimes think living with Tony would be like living in one big *Carry On* film. He only comes out with the family when there's no pressing sporting events to watch, so I can pretend he doesn't exist most of the time. Thankfully, Lola is a Fox through and through, so Tony's genes haven't had a chance to contaminate the family yet. If their second child comes out holding a remote control and smelling of Heineken and Bombay mix, that's a Crook.

Dad had bought us the ultimate Platinum package, so it was VIP the moment we got to the grounds. There was even a Range Rover to drive us the hundred metres to the entrance, which I thought was the biggest waste of time until I got out and tried walking. With every step, my gorgeous silver strappy heels sank into the grass! I looked around and saw every single woman was struggling up to the entrance. Being July, no one had figured the ground would still be soggy from the previous day's rain. Sorry, but I'm not a farmer, I'm not familiar with ground conditions. If this had been true VIP, the polo people would have texted all the women not to wear strappy or peep-toe heels. I was sorry I'd ever dissed the Range Rover because all I wanted to be driven to the bar now, but I would just have to style it out. I basically walked on tip-toes everywhere; the real skill is looking like you're not. Looking back, I can't believe I kept it up the whole day. The champagne reception took the edge off things a bit.

I think I need to explain what the event is about before I go any further. First off, I have no idea who the Duke of Essex is. He never shows up, so either he's rude or he's as real as my boobs. Secondly, no one watches any polo or knows the rules. Thirdly, there are two sections to this event: the pleb bit and VIP. The VIP area is enclosed within a pretty white picket fence. There is a really small section of the fence which the plebs can gather at and watch VIPs like zoo animals. And that's situated right by the toilets, so no famous person can go to the toilet without being yelled for. And if any celebrity is in there longer than ten minutes, the masses know what you've been doing. This was the first year the TOWIE lot had gone as proper celebrities and it completely changed the vibe of the event. It felt like a proper celebration. So much so, the polo people flew them in by helicopter to make this grand red carpet entrance. It was amazing. The entire lot of them were there except for Mark Wright and Gemma Collins. I'd never seen all of them in one place before and I proper drank it up. I can't be down on any of them for thinking they were the mutt's nuts that day because I would have been worse. I'd say the person loving the fans' attention the most was Mick Norcross, and the person loving themselves the most was Amy Childs. She walked out the toilets with bog roll attached to her heel at one point so I ran out after her before any cameras spotted her. Did I get any thanks? Did I fuck. Saying that, she must have been having an off day since a few months later, I properly met her at a party in Prezzo down Queens Road (by West Essex Law, an establish-ment is not officially recognized unless they've had a launch party with celeb guests so Prezzo's hands were tied). She was a lot more chilled out at this do since the fizz was flowing and Peter Andre showed up (without doubt, the nicest male celeb I have ever met – love him). So anyways, bottom line is I had a right laugh with her. What you see on TV is pretty much her, but the girl's got a smart business head on her. I respect that a lot and if anyone's going to stay in the limelight post-TOWIE, it's Amy.

For me, the party only truly started when Gemma rocked up with all her family in tow. I thought my family was close-knit, but the Coxes are like the Mafia. Gem's mum remarried about ten years ago, so now she's got this step-family on top of her own. And they can drink anyone under the table. So there we were, the Coxes and the Foxes on a warm July day at the starting line of a fifteen-hour bender.

It started out civilized enough, with a sit-down meal made by the bald guy off MasterChef. We got through the free bottle of wine in the first five minutes. By the time we moved to our table on the lawn to 'watch' the polo, I was smashed. I'd already lost my beloved Prada sunglasses. I don't know why I bother spending money on shades because BHQ will make me either sit on them or lose them in a horrific way. The worst has to have been when my Guccis fell off my head into the brown abyss of a V Festival Portaloo. Oh yeah, I could see them, but no way was I retrieving them, although I reckon some skank probably did. So while I clearly didn't have my wits about me, at least we had a personal hostess to wait on us. Me and the girls got sensible and ordered three pints of water and had the piss ripped out of us by our drunken parents, which is a bit wrong, isn't it?

So anyways, while we were all sat there refuelling, I felt like somebody was watching me. They totally were. I tried to focus on a group of lads who were dressed like they were going to a regatta. Blazers, blue shirts, white trousers and my worst thing, boat shoes. One of them even had a cravat on. Essex boys *love* any excuse to dress up preppy, and they could pass for a Chelsea person until they open their mouths. And then I recognized one of them, the one that looked like Freddie Ljungberg. Yeah, you got it. There was Ben just staring straight at me. I couldn't detect even a smidgeon of shame in his face. My heart started pounding so fast and I could feel my breathing get more and more shallow. After a minute, all I could say was:

'Girls, Ben's standing right over there.'

They immediately turned round.

'Turn back, you donuts! For fuck's sake, he knows we're talking about him now. He'll get off on it.'

'Fuck, what you going to do?' said Gemma.

'I'm going to have it out with the arsehole, aren't I?'

'You can do it, babe,' said Brooke, squeezing my hand. 'Here, carry this glass of champagne with you. It'll make you feel more empowered.'

I did as she instructed, even though more alcohol was the last thing I needed. I stood up, smoothed down my dress and made sure everything was in place, then I walked on the tips of my toes over to where he was, by the bar. I assumed the position – hand on hip, glass in hand.

'Well, surprise, sur-fucking-prise,' I said, giving it some attitude.

'Alright, babe?' was all he had to give back.

'Nah, I'm not alright as it so happens. I'm less than alright because you've played me for a right mug. You're a complete psycho. You just fuck around with people's heads.'

All his mates sucked in their breath and laughed.

'Shut up, will ya?' he said, turning to them. 'Come over here so we can talk private,' Ben said to me, holding me by the elbow and pulling me into a corner.

'What's wrong, hun? Can't handle women without your bitch Gino around?'

'You're a silly little girl, Becci. Stop shooting your mouth off just cos you've had a skinful,' he said, glaring at me. What a slap in the face. This was the first time I'd seen Ben show his nasty side, and it was ugly. I was a bit taken aback, to be honest, which then made me well up. I blame the champagne; it always makes me a bit emotional.

'C'mon, stop making a scene,' he said, trying to stand closer so no one could see me.

'I'm not. I don't see why I'm the silly one when you've completely disrespected me.'

'I've respected you more than anyone, hun,' he replied. 'I've said I'm sorry.'

'Oh my God, if that's ultimate respect, I'd hate to see you dissing someone. And when did you say sorry? Maybe I couldn't hear you behind that blonde that was sat on you.'

'I left a note with the flowers,' he replied, not reacting to me.

'Well I didn't get them, so I wouldn't know. What did it say?'

'I said I'm sorry for what you saw and that I hope you could get over what was, at the end of the day, a lack of communication. And then I said I'd understand if you didn't want to see me again but I'd leave the ball in your court,' he said.

'That is the worst sorry I've ever heard. You're too much of a coward to have said that to my face and you're brushing off the fact that you swopped me with that American prick like me and that girl were two vintage cars. You don't have the right to do that to people. It might have been marginally OK if I'd been landed with a hot bloke, but no, you expected me to do some old wrinkly pervert.'

'Babe, I think you're overthinking this. It was just sex and a bit of business all rolled into one.'

'Babe, I think you're underthinking this. It's not just sex, it's slave trading.'

'Well the other bird wasn't complaining, so I don't think she suffered. And I don't think you've suffered much the whole time we've been seeing each other. I've treated you well, taken you nice places and bought you pretty things. What more could you want?'

I was starting to wish I'd prepared a really coherent speech which I could shove down his throat but I was all out of argument, so I finally said, 'Well, if you don't get it, then you never will. The truth is, the only nice thing about you is your wallet. And one more thing . . . Having "family" written on your arm is proper sad.' And then I strode back to the girls all confident.

'Oh my God, did you totally own him?' said Brooke.

'One hundred per cent. He didn't know what hit him,' I replied, too ashamed to admit I'd had a less than satisfying result. I was mentally kicking myself. He actually still had a hold on me. The only solution? Drink more champagne.

Things started looking up a bit when I got a text from Ryan. He didn't have a ticket but he wanted to break into VIP. Finally, a mission. None of us could slip our wrist bands off to pass through the fence so that option was out. Because I was at that point where you're convinced everyone's your mate, I just decided to go up to friends and strangers asking them if they knew how I could get someone in. Even Micky Norcross didn't know and I thought he was Mr Essex. I was going to ask Mr Joey Essex, but he was looking a bit uptight so I left it. Then, just as I was about to ask the bald guy off MasterChef, Ben steps in my path.

'What do you want?' I said as aggressively as possible.

'Your mate just needs to tell security he's a guest of Jon's from Santander. That's how you get people in, babe.'

'Oh, good one. You using that codeword to get in a

group of escorts for later?' I said, instantly regretting the lame comment. He just walked off. Whatever. So I texted this to Ryan and before we knew it he was skipping over to our table.

'Oh my God, Ryan,' the girls yelled, 'how d'you do it?'

'It's Essex, innit!' he screamed back, and grabbed Brooke from behind and started dry-humping her.

'Way to keep a low profile,' I muttered.

'Oooh, who pulled your chain?' said Ryan, coming over to me. 'Come on, babe, let's hug it out, yeah? I'm well chuffed you got me in.'

To be fair, we all get overexcited when we blag something. It's part of the buzz. I was just pissed off that Ben could add that to the list of favours he'd done me.

❄

Around 7 p.m., the two marquees were gearing up for the after-parties. That's when the people with evening tickets flood in, and then polo gets a whole lot less glamorous. For starters, these tickets only cost £45 so they're anyone's really. If you add the evening crowd to an already sloshed day crowd, you get pure messiness. There are two different vibes to the night too. You got the Players Marquee, which is over-eighteens with big DJs playing all night, then you got the Dukes Marquee, which is 'strictly over-thirties' and puts on bands. I mean, they've made the Dukes an older crowd, but that doesn't make it any more upmarket. If that many people are tanked up on champagne, you've lost the battle.

We had a reserved booth in Dukes, and me, Mum and Tasha were dancing on the white sofas before they'd even put the music on. It was up there that I realized we were the booth behind Chantelle Houghton and Alex Reid, who were supposedly the honorary guests at the polo and apparently had ridden horses and knocked balls about during the day. I hadn't seen a thing. But once they were in the marquee drinking, I watched them like a hawk. In my opinion, it's the worst-concealed 'showmance' I've ever seen. When you start dating someone new, you can't get enough of each other. Even if you're arguing, there's chemistry. Not so Chantelle and Alex – they only perked up when their mates arrived. I will put a zillion pounds down at Paddy Power that them two don't grow old together. I'm fine with people dating people they're not into as long as they're having a good time with each other. I've done it myself and I personally find three months is the very limit. But if you look as miserable as those two in the early flushes of love, what's the point? It's their life if they think getting married and having kids is a good idea. I'm just saying that maybe her hunger for fame means she's making some odd decisions. Honestly, a proposal on TV?

However, I'm not one to talk as I clearly lost my head over Ben because I was hungry for the high life. I suppose if I'd been famous, I would have spoken out about my humiliation on *This Morning* to a sympathetic Holly and Phil. Then I'd probably reel Ryan in to be my boyfriend so I could go back on *This Morning* to gush about how I'd found love again and how we dreamed of marriage and kids. And then I'd be humiliated again when the papers ran CCTV footage of him kissing Will Young, so I'd be invited back on *This Morning* and probably *Jeremy Kyle* . . . Now I think about it, I can see how addictive it all is.

My surveillance was interrupted by Gemma, who fell up the step into our booth. Classy. 'Is your brother here yet?' she asked.

'Yeah, he came in here earlier, but he's with his mates in the Players Marquee now,' I replied.

'Why don't we go over there and see him?' she said.

I was all suspicious by this point because she'd never shown any interest in Jake before, but I humoured her. We gathered up the other two and made our way over just as the heavens decided to open. It went mental, with everyone racing around, tripping over tables just to get undercover. By the time we got to Players, we were drenched through. The others were laughing hysterically, but I sobered up as soon as I realized my big hair had died. Epic flatness. I tried to put it in the back of my mind when I spotted Jake raving it up like a lunatic. When I pointed him out to Gemma, she looked disappointed.

'Is Jamie not there then?' she asked.

'I don't think so, hun. You not heard from him then?' I asked, suddenly getting her agenda.

'Nothing. And I didn't get his number either.'

'I can totally get it off Jake for you if you like?'

'Nah, don't worry about it,' she replied, looking defeated.

I know that feeling when you've made a real effort because you've imagined this bloke's going to be there that night, and you're all geared up for the first moment he sees you but instead you're faced with disappointment because he's a no-show. We've all been there. But the thing is, there was somebody looking adoringly at Gemma, but she hadn't seen Grant yet. When I pointed him out, her face dropped. Had I totally misjudged this one?

'What's *he* doing here,' she hissed.

'It's a free country, Gem. Anyone can come if they can afford a ticket,' said Brooke.

'Oh shit, he's coming over,' said Gemma, gathering herself. Me and Brooke slowly backed away from the scene as it was clearly about to kick off. We went into the crowd and hit the dance floor.

I had to do a double-take when I saw Jake's dancing companion was Tasha. They properly don't get on. She thinks he's a waste of space and he thinks she's a snob. They're both right. But you know what, alcohol can really reunite a family sometimes, especially when a song plays that allows you all to indulge in the Essex

Shuffle. Anyone who clubbed in Essex in the Nineties will have blocked this exotic dance from their memory. To make it work, you'd need some garage tunes going on, something like 'Sweet Like Chocolate' by Shanks & Bigfoot or anything by MJ Cole. The Shuffle was only done by women and required you to hold your purse like a dumb-bell in your leading hand. You'd then move your hand in a motion that looked like you were open-ing and closing a drawer. You'd alternate that move with a subtle bounce and a step. You'd bounce-step for-ward like this with your purse-hand still going, and then you'd bounce-step back again. Your face could never show any sign of excitement, just a bored look of disdain. And that's the Essex Shuffle. It couldn't be done to anything energetic like Baby D's 'Let Me Be Your Fantasy'. That would have been a major faux pas.

Tasha used to come back from places like the Castle in Woodford or the Country Club in Chigwell and get me and Jake doing it with her in the living room. I wanted her life so badly, but my first club experience in Faces in 2000 was the exact moment the Essex Shuffle was being phased out. I mean, I witnessed it, but I didn't see it in its heyday. Gutted! So, despite our differences, the Essex Shuffle is one thing that bonds the Fox kids. When they played that Nineties club classic in the Players Marquee, the place didn't know what had hit them. We were off. But I stopped in my bounce-step tracks when I could feel someone staring at me. I was hoping it wasn't Ben, but to my horror it was much worse. Bloody Bucket.

I should have known Vicki P. would pop up at some point that evening. She was looking at my dance moves like this was how I seriously danced. So I just danced harder and let her know I was having a good time. Bucket hates nothing more than girls enjoying themselves.

After about twenty minutes of dancing, I thought I'd go and check on how Gemma was doing. I did a slow walk past and heard Grant say, 'How many girls do you know who got an engagement ring *and* satnav?' As lines went for winning back a girl, it wasn't the best, so I didn't have high hopes for this ending happily.

I was so done with the Players so headed back to the Dukes Marquee. Brooke and Ryan were already back in the booth. Clearly they'd disassociated themselves from me as soon as they saw me doing the Shuffle. Mum and Dad were on the dance floor twirling around to some band called Kid Creole and the Coconuts. Don't ask, but my parents love this man and used to play his music so loud when we were kids. He was the main reason they'd come to the polo, if you can believe that. He was just an old man with three young birds singing tropical songs. I didn't get it.

'Your mum is such a mover,' said Brooke.

'Tell her that, she'll be well chuffed,' I said. She was looking lovely in this strapless white dress.

'Look at the pins on her too, and such a tiny waist,' said Ryan admiringly.

'She did used to be a professional ice-skater, you know.'

'*Shut up*,' Brooke and Ryan said in unison.

'Swear to God, she was up there with Jayne Torvill.'

'Awww, they're so sweet together. I hope I end up like that,' Brooke said, spilling champagne on herself.

I haven't even told you the Don and Jackie Fox love story yet, have I? Picture this: it's the late 1970s and there's Mum looking like Jo Wood and Dad's there looking like Harrison Ford. They were so beautiful. Dad was a bit of a player and he'd worked his way through most of the women in Essex, which is why him and his mates went for a night of ice-skating in South London. They were after fresh blood. They get there all mouthy and lairy when Dad clocks Mum doing this incredible skating display. Dad claims he said to his mate, 'That's the girl I'm going to marry.' So he kept going back there until she noticed him. He was completely under her spell. See, that's what I mean about players. It only takes one woman at the right time.

Finally Mum caved in and started dating him, but she was doing ice-skating tours around the country which meant Dad was pining for her. In the end, he said she had to give it up if she wanted them to be together, and she did! She quit her passion for another passion. Oh, and then she got up the duff with Tasha so that really put an end to the skating, and then they got married. And then they had two more children by accident too. After Jake, Mum made Dad get the snip. I think they would have been quite happy if it had been just the two of them, to be honest, because they are the most in-love old people you'll ever see. Mum once told me that the secret to a happy marriage is this: always make an effort with your appearance, don't nag and never act jel. I thought that sounded a bit old-fashioned, but then I realized Mum avoids major conflicts yet she gets her own way all the time. She's no martyr, just a tactical genius.

Although, when it comes to looking good, I have two issues with her. First, she will walk into my cottage when I'm not there and borrow clothes for her nights out with the First Wives Club. I mean, I'm so happy she can fit into them, but it's proper annoying. The other issue is her dabbles with facial surgery. I was so traumatized in 1996 when she came home after her first session of Botox, I actually cried. I was only twelve, so give me a break. I felt disturbed because she *looked* disturbed with this super-tight forehead and stunned expression. It was so tight that it made her cheeks look proper saggy too. Then she tried to correct that by putting fillers in her cheeks, so she looked like a chipmunk. The only thing that worked was the eyelift. She got it done down the road at Holly House, which is where I got my boobs done (as did Amy Childs and

Jessica Wright), and I reckon it took fifteen years off her. They're good there at improving your look while keeping it natural. I didn't want Jordan-sized knockers, just boobs that were a natural tear-drop shape. Spherical melons that look like they've been stuck on are so naff.

Anyways, Mum was really pleased with the result, but in my opinion she still needs to lay off the Botox. It doesn't make you look younger, but it does make you look rich. If I see a motionless face, I think, they've got money to burn, and I will target those same women at a wedding fair. Although Mum's not half as bad as Cheryl and Sue. You don't even notice the amount of Botox they've had because their lips are so gigantic. They honestly look like something out of the Muppets.

Talking of which, I'd not spoken to Jake about Sue at any point because I still found it sickening. But when she and Cheryl showed up for the evening's entertainment, I spotted her and Jake having a whispered row outside, which unfortunately backed up Dad's gossip. So I later cornered Jake about all this because I'd had a few drinks and felt brave enough to hear the very worst. He completely exploded.

'How do you know about that?' he hissed at me.

'People tell me stuff, hun.'

'Well, don't tell no one else. All that happened was she gave me a couple of blowies, nothing more.'

'That's grim,' I said, trying to force my mind to go blank.

'You wanna hear something grim? She just came up to me and went, "So you fancy having your lolly washed again?" She's fucking filth.'

'Oh, look who's got all prudish all of a sudden,' I laughed, but he didn't see the funny side. 'So how you going to deal with this one then?'

'I've already told her to do one or I'm telling Mum.'

'Oh cool, so your usual tactic of using Mum for protection. Do you reckon she'll listen?'

'She'd better or I'll rip out her new carpets,' he said, trying to be all menacing. He so can't pull off hard talk.

I hoped Mum would never find out or there'd be the biggest showdown Buckhurst Hill had ever seen.

When I went back in to the Dukes Marquee, Mum and Dad were still dancing. Then I looked over to our reserved area and there was Brooke sat on Charlie's lap. Why had nobody even told me he was coming?

This was the first time I'd seen them together and it was like a stab in the chest. Yes I knew about it, but we'd never spoken about it and I'd never had visual evidence, so it was like it wasn't real. There was no denying it now. My best friend and my ex were seriously getting it on right before me. Even when I went over, she didn't climb off him. So I sat there like a right lemon trying to think of things to say. I gabbled on about Gemma and Grant, Chantelle and Alex, I told them about the girl I'd seen stamping around in shoes like hooves and how I'd seen one girl in a white dress slip in the mud. They nodded like they were just waiting for me to go. I felt like complete shit. They weren't making it easy for me, and I think Charlie sensed this because he suddenly went, 'Brooke, why don't you get the drinks in?' and she looked all suspicious. What did she think I was going to do? Jump him?

'Alright, but don't go anywhere.'

We had waitress service at our table, but I wasn't about to tell *her* that.

After a minute of silence, I actually wanted Brooke to come back again. 'So this is awkward,' I said finally.

'Yeah, sorry. I meant to come over earlier but couldn't find you. And you haven't been down One9Five for a while, so it's sort of weird,' he said.

'Oh, don't worry. Even my best friend hasn't had a word with me about this yet. It's the greatest unspoken romance of all time,' I replied, proper pass-agg.

'I thought you two were cool with each other?' he replied, looking puzzled.

'Yeah, we were, but only because we've avoided talking about it. And now I've just had to confront it in the worst possible way,' I replied.

He paused before saying, 'Welcome to my world, babe. Not easy seeing your ex get cosy with someone else, is it?' I definitely heard a wobble in his voice and I thought, shit, he's getting emotional. I'd never seen Charlie cry before and I wouldn't know what to do, so I changed the subject quickly.

'No matter, hun. So did you come down here with Grant?'

'He needed someone to hold his hand, didn't he? He's been a right old mess,' said Charlie.

'Well he should think twice before cheating,' I said, and instantly regretted it. Major hypocrite. I don't know when things got so awkward between us, but at this moment it felt like an all-time low in our relationship.

It was so strange to think how close we were just three years ago and now we were like strangers. Believe it or not, we did have the funniest times together. Like when I went back to his for the first time and he only had one pillow as thin as cardboard on his double bed and nothing but a harsh overhead light. Proper passion-killer. I totally made his life more comfortable and bought him four fluffy pillows and a lovely lamp for his side table. Clearly I benefited from this too, but think of the favour I did all the girls who came after me. Yeah, you're welcome, Brooke.

And we would have such a laugh when we went out. One night when Charlie Ferrari was truly living up to his name, we were desperately after some class As, so someone hooked us up with a dealer who met us in the car park behind the Castle. Gone were the days when it was West Essex's number-one night spot. Now it's a glamorous Harvester. In fact, this was the same car park that Victoria and David Beckham met in for their first date. They were going to go to the Castle (not for a

Harvester) but realized there was a pap around, so David jumped into her MG and they went to a curry house in Chingford. Why does the Castle not have some sort of blue plaque marking this historical moment?

Anyways, we exchanged money and drugs there and drove back to Charlie's to get a fix before heading out. Well it was only bloody Daz. When Charlie realized he went, 'At least we'll have the cleanest noses in Essex now.' Fuck, I've never laughed so hard in all my days. I didn't even need any drugs after that. Just his company would give me a major high. And now here he was, the bloke he'd been before the steroids took over. He might not have the rage any more, but I did. I had to put up with some real nastiness at the end of our relationship and Brooke had just waltzed in as the going had got good again. Talk about complicated. It's not like I wanted Charlie back, but still, it's a bit rich, isn't it?

When I saw Ryan stumbling over to us I felt proper relieved, but then he didn't know what to say either. He just stood over us and went, 'Awww, exes.' After dropping that clanger, he just waltzed off and left us feeling even more uncomfortable. I was actually ecstatic when I saw Brooke come back because she was looking well pissed off. I needed one of Brooke's incidents to get me out of this situation.

'What's the matter?' I said to her.

'Your sister is the matter,' Brooke replied, stabbing a finger at my shoulder. 'Her husband is making a right dick of himself on the dance floor. Like, people are actually backing away from him because he's so out of it. So I just went over to Tasha and said, "You wanna keep an eye on your fella," and she just yelled at me, "What's it got to do with you?" So I just walked away and left them to it, but hun, your sister has serious issues.'

'Shit, I can't believe she spoke to you like that,' I said, embarrassed for my clan.

'Yer, well, I had to hold my tongue. But in other news, I seen Gem and Grant snogging.'

'Oh my God, you joking? You serious?' I said.

'I'm totally serious. Wedding's back on, people,' she said and kissed Charlie. She was totally marking her territory. If she wanted to be like that, then fine. I've always been the stronger one of us, so not a problem.

'Right, I'm going to find Tasha and sort her out,' I said to them.

'Well, good luck to yer,' said Brooke. 'I was saying to Gem and Ryan we should get out of here after midnight and head down One9Five for the after-party.'

'But then we'll miss Arg singing,' I whined.

'Do you seriously want to watch him? He's not all that, babe,' said Brooke, shattering the illusion as usual.

'I suppose not. I just thought it would be a laugh. I mean, I don't want to be here until the very end,' I replied, trying to convince myself. To be honest, I needed to talk to Ben again so I was dragging my feet. Something was niggling. Although there was no way I was going to be here when the music stopped at 2 a.m. You have to be completely stupid to think you can get a cab then. I've known people resort to staggering back to Epping High Street along the dark country lanes. If they're lucky, it'll take them two hours to do so and they'll look like they've crawled out of a ditch. If they're unlucky, they'll get mown down by a taxi.

When I couldn't find Tasha in either of the marquees, I made my way through the mud to the toilets. If she was having a meltdown, that's where she'd be. Right outside the toilets, I noticed there was a film crew talking to some drunk girl who had her baps hanging out, so I went over to earwig and the shit she was coming out with was embarrassing. I'll give you a taster: 'Yeah, well, I don't think I'm going to find myself a husband at the polo. I'd give the quality of men here a five out of ten. They're all too short here and they love themselves too much. Whoever gets with me has to be as good as me. I'm nice looking so they got to be nice looking too.'

Let me tell you, this girl was a mess. I'd already seen her earlier in the day in a green dress, and now she was wearing this horrible slutty black dress which had cups that just about covered her nipples, and she had scruffy dirty blonde hair with no volume whatsoever. She was no lady but her standards were high. I wanted to go, 'Have a word with yourself, love.'

She also had this more glam mate with wavy blonde

hair who'd had so much surgery she looked like a blow-up doll. As soon as they were done filming, I asked the cameraman who he worked for and he said the same production company that had done *My Big Fat Gypsy Wedding*. I think we can safely say that they were setting this silly girl up for a fall. So I said to him, 'You've got yourself a goldmine with that girl,' and he just looked proper pleased with himself.

I would never in a million years appear in a documentary, especially now everyone's after a piece of the Essex goodness. I imagine this one will be titled *Essex Husband-Hunting* so watch this space. And the talent was so not five out of ten either. Maybe that was just her success rate.

Realizing I'd been distracted by my nosiness, I got back to my family duties. I poked my head into each cabin until I saw the legs of my sister's white jumpsuit and her strappy silver heels.

'Alright, Tash?' I said, tapping on the door.

'Yeah, you?' she said, clearly mid-sob.

'Seriously, Tash, you don't sound alright. You going to let me in or what?'

There was no answer, just a bit of sniffling. Then the lock went. What I saw . . . I can't even put into words. There was still a bit of sick in the corner of her mouth just to complete the look.

'Shit, Tash. I think you need to go home,' I said, not knowing what to do.

'Why is this happening?' she cried. 'Why would it do this?'

'Who's doing what?'

'Why's the mud doing all this? It's not fair. I can't even see my feet,' she slurred back.

'Well at least they're a lovely shade of brown. And somehow you've managed not to get any mud on your clothes,' I said, trying to make her feel better.

'I haven't even had sex for seven months,' she said randomly.

'Isn't that normal though when you've got a toddler?' I asked.

'I want Tony to want me like he used to,' she said. I had to wipe the sick off her mouth before I could interact any more with her.

'Look, you just need time together. I never look after Lola, but I can do that for you if you want,' I said.

'Really? Even on a Saturday night?'

'Yeah, totally.' I agreed to it, but there was no way she'd remember in the morning. I just wanted to get her sobered up a bit. 'C'mon, let's get out of here and find Tony, yeah?'

'Nah, I'm not going. You've got to find Tony and bring him here,' she demanded.

'Seriously? Oh my God, the things I do for you. Fine, but then you've both got to come with me.'

She nodded but just slumped her head down between her legs. I noticed all these pound coins on the floor around her so I gathered them up before heading off. Old habits die hard. You could make your money back from your ticket with the amount of shrapnel on the floors here.

Now, when I set off, I had no intention of finding Tony. That was a disaster waiting to happen. I was going to do a Jake and rely on Mum to sort it out. She's the only one who Tasha obeys. It was pissing it down again and the mud was making it proper dangerous out there. Next time, I'd be bringing a pair of Weddingtons. They're white wellies designed for brides with a well cute heel and ribbon on. I was so getting them in stock even if it was just for me. My feet were as bad as Tasha's, but I just had to squelch my way back to the marquee.

It was proper mayhem outside the marquees. A group of blokes were clapping and chanting for another bloke to hurdle the white picket fence. And since blokes love showing off to each other, this prat totally did it and impaled himself. Who jumps *out* of VIP? I had zero sympathy.

When I got indoors, I found Gemma at her table in the family fold. It looked like Gem's step-dad was giving Grant a serious man-to-man chat. Her step-dad is short, squat, bald and hard as nails. He was probably telling Grant that if he cheated on Gemma again, he'd rip off his scrotum with his bare hands. That's his standard threat and Grant did look petrified.

'Have you seen Jackie anywhere?' I said to Gem.

'She's leading the conga with Ryan.' Oh the shame, she was and all. Ryan's a proper bad influence and he was trying to get Cheryl and Sue involved too.

'Oh my days, I'm disowning her and him. So you and Grant, yeah?'

'I know. Don't be mad at me. I can't help going back to him,' she said, oblivious to my matchmaking. 'The last ten weeks and five days have been the most miserable in my life. And it's well difficult out there, Becs. I don't know how you keep it up,' she said.

'We're just different people, Gem. Honestly, I'm proper made up for you. If he's what makes you more happy than sad then you've got to go for it. And maybe he'll appreciate you more now?'

'Yeah, well, I never have been able to resist his charms.' Having heard his charms, I can safely say me and Gem are not cut from the same cloth. Satnav, I ask you.

'You do know that Ben keeps looking over at you?' Gemma said.

'Oh my God, is he? Who's he with?' I asked.

'He's just leaning on the barrier by himself. He's totally trying to get your attention. What you going to do?'

'I really don't give a shit,' I said, lying. 'I'm going to go over there and tell him to bog off.'

'God, such a nightmare having to fight off all these hot men,' she said mocking me.

'Well, I can't control who looks, hun. I just bring the heat.'

I turned round and Ben was doing the puppy-dog-eyes thing at me. We've all seen that trick before. But for once he genuinely looked remorseful. So I went over to him and said, 'Where's your entourage gone? Have they gone to pick up some birds for you?'

'Don't be like that, Becs,' he said, like I was being unreasonable. 'I already know I've been a right tool, but we can't end things like this.'

'You already decided how to end things.'

'I took things too far, I know, and I got you all wrong. But no girl's got to me like this before.'

'Oh, come off it, Ben. You're just not used to girls giving you a hard time.'

'Nah, I'm serious. Out of all the fifty-six girls I've slept with, you're different.'

'Oh my God, you've slept with fifty-six girls? What kind of person even counts that shit once they get into double figures? That's proper sad.'

'All blokes do it, babe. And if you do the maths, that's only an average of eight a year.'

'Unbelievable. Ben, I've slept with that many in my whole life. Your mind's all warped.' (That figure's honestly true, give or take a couple, so long as we're talking standard intercourse.) 'If that's how you boost your ego, then I pity you.'

'Nah, but you're not listening. I don't want to be that bloke any more. I just want you.'

'Are you shitting me? Are you saying you want me to be your girlfriend now?'

'That's exactly what I'm saying, babe. I want to do this properly and I only want to do it with you.'

I didn't know what to say back to this. It totally threw me. I had him at my beck and call, but then I thought he could just be fobbing me off again. He could tell I was deliberating my next move, so he tried to make it for me.

'Listen, come back to mine. We'll sort it out there.'

'Ben, you can't expect me to come back with you after the way you've treated me,' I said.

Ben actually looked cut up.

Perfect timing as always, Ryan came running over to interrupt. 'Babe, the cab's coming in ten minutes,' he said before turning to Ben. 'Hiya, Ben. She sent me your picture so I know you even though you don't know me. You're way fitter in person. Thanks for getting me in. Byers,' and with that the whirlwind was off. What was it with Ryan leaving trails of destruction everywhere he went? You can't have the upper hand when it's obvious you've been perving with your mates over a photo that was for your eyes only.

'What picture's he talking about?' said Ben

'Just that modelling picture you sent me where you wore those tight pants,' I replied, trying to sound casual.

'We were just checking your picture out once. It's nothing. He's gay, by the way, so it's all above board.'

'Yeah, I'm not blind. He's flapping all over the place. You girls and gays are all the same. Can't get on with them myself. No offence.'

'I so pity you,' I said, suddenly feeling a lot of offence. 'Like, it might surprise you that Ryan's a season-ticket holder at Spurs. He's as boring as any straight man on the subject. He's an awesome gambler and would totally show you up at poker. He could make your iPhone do things you never dreamed it could do. And he's an amazing friend, something you'll never know because girls are just trophies and gays are just flappers. Oh, but Gino, he's someone you can look up to? What a sad little life you have putting people in boxes. You are blind, actually.'

'Sorry, have I really annoyed you?'

'*Yes, you fucking have*,' I yelled.

'Listen, I take back what I said. I'm trying so hard to sort things out here, but I can't seem to say anything right,' he said, looking really shocked by my tirade. 'I think you're right, babe, I haven't being seeing the whole picture. That's why I need you back in my life.'

I still had nothing to say back to this.

'Just think about it. If you want to give me a shout later on, then I'll be about.'

Then he kissed me on the cheek and walked off into the rain. I felt like he was totally messing with my mind again, but hadn't I wanted this sort of resolution? After all, I was the cool one again now. Finally.

However, I couldn't be standing around trying to decipher all this now. I spotted Mum hanging off Dad in the distance, so I squelched over to her to do my only good deed.

'Mum, Tasha's in the toilets and she's puked down her face,' I said, keeping it nice and short.

'The silly girl. She can't take her drink any more, but does she listen to me?' Mum moaned.

'Listen, I'm going off with the others now. So you know where Tash is, yeah? Where's Jake?' I asked.

'He's pulling yet another girl. Being a mum is a never-ending, thankless task, you know. Why are my kids alcoholics and love rats?' she moaned.

'Hmmm, I'd say that's a bit over the top,' I said.

'Darlin', we were young once, remember?' butted in Dad. 'They've got to go out there and live life to the full. And our little Becs is doing alright for herself, aren't you, princess?'

'Yeah, just brilliant, Dad. I've got to go. See you in the morning, yeah?' And with that I ran off to join the others.

There were only four people in the taxi queue, which was a result, so we hardly had to wait at all. One girl in front of us turned to her bloke and went, 'Alfie, I'll never wear these fucking shoes again. You try dressing for the occasion but this shitty mud ain't no fun, you know what I mean? It's like being a student or something. VIP should mean privilege. My feet aren't even in my shoes no more.' And she just whined on and on. You can give a WEG the most VIP day ever, but she won't feel complete unless she's had a proper moan. As the couple got into the taxi, the girl went, 'I tell you what, though, Alfie. I didn't see one fight tonight,' and with that she closed the door. I could tell she was disappointed by how civil the night had been, but as far as I was concerned it had been clash after clash.

So we did go to One9Five, and after thirty minutes I walked out the club and made a booty call. I can only think I did this because I was proper irritated by how much action everyone else was getting. Everyone had paired up and my surrogate boyfriend Ryan had just Grindred a man and was currently chatting him up at the bar. You got to understand, I was in the club I first laid eyes on this exotic racing driver, so yes, I went back to Ben's, but it's not how it looks.

Swear to God I knew exactly what I was doing.

13

Mug Them off What Mugged You

When your head is thick from excess champagne, there's no better place to be than by the pool at the Kings Oak. I rocked up there the following afternoon for food and to dissect the day before. I was road-testing my Marbs look which was a pink bikini with denim hot pants, but I left the flies open and pulled the flap to one side. This was the poolside look that was going around that summer, trust me. Then I put my hair in a cute loose fishtail plait. Who needs Marbs when you got your own Nikki Beach in the middle of Epping Forest? As with everywhere that's worth going to in West Essex, you got to be a member if you want to get involved. You can sit by the pool if you got £300 to spare, but don't bother going for a swim. For one, the pool is well cold. For two, you're there to sunbathe and be seen. Why they didn't film the famous *TOWIE* pool party here, I don't know. It's the perfect size pool to have pushed Mark Wright into. Perhaps they couldn't afford it.

Obviously Russ got himself into the background of this scene, so I know they filmed it at some random house in Chingford. Not so glam! They did film Chloe's wedding-themed thirtieth birthday there because it's pretty classy inside. Anyways, I walked in with Marilyn and the others were already there. It all fell silent as I walked towards them, so clearly they'd been talking about me. So obvious.

'Alright, people?' I said cheerfully.

'Yeah, you?' said Brooke.

'Yeah, not so bad. I had a pretty eventful night, as you can imagine.'

'How come you borrowed Brooke's nail glue before you left last night?' asked Gem.

'I needed it for a little project.'

'Oh yeah, spill,' said Gem.

'Well, I did go back to Ben's, but it was only so I could get closure,' I paused. 'And a bit of loving. You know that feisty sex you have when you're all angry but hot for someone? It was that. But I made sure I was the most selfish lover Essex has ever seen. I gave absolutely nothing of myself to him unless I got pleasure from it.'

'It's the least you deserve, hun,' Ryan said, chipping in.

'So after I'd had a good seeing-to, I got up in the very early hours to empty his drawer of smut into a bag. Then I used your glue to attach his shagging trophies to his Mercedes. As expected, my eyelash glue didn't cut it, which is why I needed your nail glue. Sorry, I used it all up, hun.'

'Like I care . . . So it was you! I knew there was a commotion by Ben's place this morning, but I couldn't see.'

'Well, the unwashed thongs stuck particularly well to the car. I think the dildo will come away quite easily, so long as he doesn't mind it taking the paintwork with it. Oh, I nearly forgot – I also smashed up all his man make-up. He'll probably be more cut-up about that, the vain prick.'

'Oh my God, he got owned *and* served. You're such a bad girl, Becs,' said Ryan, screaming.

'Yeah, I think we can draw a line under that one since he'll now think I'm the biggest bitch alive, but that's fine because he's the biggest nobhead alive.'

'Fuck, I'm never messing with you,' said Brooke, who genuinely looked scared. I'm not surprised after the way she behaved with Charlie in front of me. I'd felt a proper heaviness in my heart, and not because I wanted Charlie for myself. I wasn't sure what it was, to be honest.

'So now I can see clearly again, there's only one thing

on my mind now and that's Gem's hen do,' I said. 'We're going to give you the best send-off ever.'

'I should hope so too since I'm throwing a wedding party that'll put Kate and Wills' little shindig to shame,' Gem replied.

We only had three weeks to make arrangements. I'd been severely delayed by the wedding being called off.

'Hun, you and me should get back down the gym before Puerto Banus, yeah?' Ryan said suddenly. 'Now that you're feeling more up to it, it'll be good for you. And Gem's coming down to get in shape for the wedding.'

'Oh yeah, I was wondering when you were going to bring that up again,' I said, ready for a fight. 'Absolutely no piggin' way am I stepping foot in that gym again. Did being buff do me any favours? No. I'm not doing it. I'm sticking to the Shit Yourself Thin diet. I don't know why you don't just do that too, Gem.'

'Well, Ryan said he thought he could get me to Jennifer Aniston's league in time for the wedding . . .'

'Save it, I've heard it all before,' I said, shaking my head at Ryan. I was on to him now. He basically preys on vulnerable women facing major events in their lives. What a dirty trick.

✳

So what did I achieve in those three weeks? Not a lot. I sent an email round about the theme and dress code, which would be interesting considering a couple of the ladies were plus-sized. So the hens would be me, Gem, Brooke and Ryan, obviously. Then Cleo was going to join as well as the other three bridesmaids, posh Emily, Gem's cousin Paula, Gem's sister Karen plus their mum Linda. What a rag-tag crew.

But there was an interesting development in the romance department. We had a huge family barbecue round ours for Dad's birthday, which meant a lot of Foxes were in our back garden. Since Dad likes to take over these events, me, Tasha and Jake just chilled on sunloungers as he sweated over hot coals.

The truth of the matter is, Dad won't let us near his barbecues because we all have previous when it comes to cooking. Jake once made cheese on toast in a toaster. To be fair to him, he did put it on its side so the cheese didn't slide down, but it still blew up. And Tasha made hot chocolate by putting milk in the electric kettle once. Again, she was successful. But the stench. Believe it or not, I'm like Delia Smith compared to them two. My only sin is that I'm cack-handed and fall into things, so I'm not allowed near fires of any sort, and, as you know already, candles are the bane of my life. Dad's never forgiven me for knocking over the giant floor-candelabra when it was fully lit. In my defence, those things really don't give out good light, so how am I supposed to see where I'm going? Poor Don. Yet another carpet destroyed by yours truly. Anyway, if you make yourself a calamity in the kitchen, then people tend to cook for you. And that's how it was possible for all three Fox kids to kick back with cocktails in the July sunshine.

Tony had a Grand Prix to watch so he couldn't make it, thank God. But talk about rubbing salt in an open wound. Just the words 'Grand Prix' make me think of Ben and I annoy myself every time I get sucked into watching a race. As long as Ben never makes it to F1, it's bearable.

Anyways, Tasha left to go find Lola, who was no doubt giving some aunt the run-around. Jake turns to me and goes, 'You know my mate Jamie?'

'What about him?'

'Well, he's an alright fella, you know. Just in case you were interested,' he said.

'Oh my God, are you giving me permission?'

'If you want to look at it that way, then yeah. But just shows that I really respect him because I wouldn't let any Tim, Mick or Barry go after my sister,' he said.

'How do you know him anyway?'

'He's my partner in the Chinese lantern business, ain't he? We did the deal in Thailand together. But now his music career's properly taking off. Like, he's mates with that Taio Cruz.'

'Oh my God, Taio Cruz was in Monaco. That's why Jamie was out there! Shit, that's amazing,' I gasped.

'Oh yeah, now you're interested.'

'Oh shut up, I'm not as shallow as that, hun. In fact,

I've sworn off men for the rest of the year. I just want to focus on me for a bit. I need to get back to the way I was.'

'So you weren't focusing on you before? Interesting,' said Jake, smirking.

'Oh pipe down, you. I mean it, I'm serious. I'm not being messed around no more or I'll turn into Brooke.'

I was actually proper worried about that. It's like the universe had been turned upside down where I was getting shat on and Brooke was being wined and dined. I'd come to the conclusion that Ben had one hundred per cent dickmatized me, and to break the trance I needed to start calling the shots again when it came to blokes. It wasn't going to happen overnight, but I hoped being with the girls in our old stomping ground of Puerto Banus would awaken my previous self. All I wanted was to be treated with respect and not be traded off as part of a business deal. Was that too much to ask?

At least I'd paired Gemma back with Grant now, so if I wanted, I could have a clear run at Jamie. Not that I wanted that because, honestly, I was just going to focus on having fun with my friends.

Although I've got to say, hen dos are such a headache. I don't know who came up with them. I really needed BHQ to lay off me for this one, but they clearly sensed my weariness and decided to fuck things up for me from start to finish. To say the trip was a challenge would be an understatement. Our flight to Malaga was at 7 a.m. with Ryanair. Since we all got there in the middle of the night, we had plenty of time for breakfast and our first cocktail of the trip, which I made Gemma drink using her willy straw.

Weirdly, none of us had really been paying attention to the time. At 6.30 a.m., I thought, shit, we should be at the gate, so I gathered everyone up and we were there ten minutes later.

'Where is everybody?' I asked the woman at the desk.

'Everyone's on the plane and the flight's now closed,' she said coldly.

'What do you mean? It doesn't go for another twenty minutes,' I said.

'It was a quiet flight so we boarded everyone. You can't go on.'

'But it's her hen do. You can't do this,' I pleaded.

'The rules clearly state . . .'

'Oh shove the rules up your bum,' said Brooke, wading in. 'From one steward to another, this is really shabby, especially as I know you haven't even closed the doors to the plane yet. You've obviously got issues and are taking it out on us.'

By this point, Gemma was trying to keep a brave face but was on the verge of crumbling, so I had to take over.

'C'mon, let's just get another flight. It's all part of the adventure,' I said, and marched off to the Ryanair front desk.

I won't lie, it was a major palaver. They had to get our bags off the flight (surely easier to have put us on it), then we had to be walked round to check-in again. Turned out there were no more flights to Malaga that day. Not even Brooke with her easyJet connections could make it happen. So we had to pay those Ryanair a-holes £100 for the privilege of going to Seville, which then involved a two-hour drive to Puerto Banus. I felt like I'd let everyone down, even though they said I wasn't to blame. So I thought, yeah, it's your fault actually since you know I have this disability which means I can't understand time. One in four people have it. Just saying.

The only other hen do I've been on was my sister's, where we hired a barge on the Norfolk broads and did a pub crawl. Since I didn't organize that one, I didn't feel too bad about that near-disaster. The problem was, we all knew how to start the thing, but nobody had listened when the owner was telling us how to stop it. We asked every barge coming in the opposite direction, but they'd all gone past before they finished telling us. It was like that film *Speed* but on a barge. Nobody could help us and we were passing all these pubs we wanted to drink at. Eventually a stag do caught up with us and showed us how to do it, but by that point we were all sober and it was dark. It turned out alright in the end as we joined forces with the stags and Tasha ended up snogging their groom. That's what I was hoping for with this hen do. I could deal with a bad start so long as we were all pissed up and laughing about it hours later.

Except when we got to Puerto Banus, we were all too broken to remember what laughter was. It was 4 p.m., so essentially we'd been travelling for nine hours. What a joke. Not even the first sight of the harbour in the blazing July sun could lift our spirits. I thought, as soon as they see the amazing apartment I've hired and we're out drinking fizz on the terrace, all will be good in the world.

The owner was waiting outside for us.

'I'm afraid there's a change of plan. I'm going to have to give you a different apartment, but it's just as nice,' he said cheerily.

'What you saying?' said Brooke.

'Unfortunately, your apartment got trashed by another hen do last weekend and until we clean it up, it's not fit for anyone to stay in. But you won't even notice the difference between the two places.'

So we dragged our huge suitcases up four flights of stairs to our new apartment. I was mortified. There was no balcony and one of us would have to sleep on the sofa. I'd been dreaming of that balcony, but instead we were faced with two nights in this windowless dark flat. I spent the next hour arguing with the bloke because he wanted to charge us the same price. I needed to win at least one battle that day, so I stood firm in my negotiations. Once I'd threatened to hold him hostage all Saturday night, he gave in. By the time that was all sorted, it was 5.30 p.m. and everyone was half ready except me.

I was well unhappy with how I was looking by 7 p.m. I hate it when you're all done up except for your face, because the contrast makes you look proper ugly. I felt bad but I had to do my make-up during the drinking games. Cleo and Emily insisted on doing these 'getting to know you' games, which was just lame because I knew everyone.

The much anticipated theme was the Playboy Bunnies and Hugh Hefner, aka Ryan. We were all in tight black hot pants and corsets with bunny-girl ears, and, as is tradition, we trussed up Gem in a bride-to-be sash, a veil and flashing learner plates. She looked a picture. Ryan actually trumped her with his maroon smoking jacket and pipe. The sleeves were bursting at the seams as they tried to contain them guns of his. He looked like the Incredible Hulk on his way to a gentleman's club. Hugh Hefner *wishes* he looked like that. Karen and Paula let the team down a bit by coming out in crocheted black dresses which went down to the floor. They didn't seem to have a problem with wearing identical clothes. I can't even wear the same *style* outfit as someone, let alone the same one. Luckily, Gem's mum didn't do hot pants either.

When you see a hen do out and about, you always find it's the ones with kids who behave the worst because it's like they've been released into singledom for a limited time. This crew was no exception. Karen and Paula had five kids between them. You'd have thought Gem's mum Linda would be a calming influence, but she was the most out of control. By the time we left the apartment they were hammered and Linda was wearing Gemma's veil and learner plates. Total nightmare. Emily was looking proper horrified by it all and had already been moaning how uncomfortable she felt going out dressed like a bunny. I told her to suck it up and just do it for Gemma.

For those of you who haven't experienced the joys of Puerto Banus, let me explain. By day, PB is a pretty town. The streets are crammed with Gucci, Missoni and Fendi, the marina is lined up with expensive yachts, and the bars and clubs charge extortionate prices. So basically, it's like Essex-on-Sea, only it's part Euro, part trash. Comfortably nestled amongst the glitz and glamour lies a proper seedy side to PB that fully emerges at night time. My dad did have a timeshare out here but he got rid of it because he said the place had gone downhill. In some ways it has, but in other ways, debauchery isn't always such a bad thing.

The waterfront is always pretty civilized, but since we'd all lost our buzz there was only one option: Linekers. Yeah, it's owned by Gary Lineker's brother. He was banged up for tax fraud a few years back, but he still seems to own half of Puerto Banus. Clearly jail didn't do him any damage. The place was rammed with hen dos that had reserved areas with these tacky personalized banners. There were girls dressed in burlesque outfits and another group in US marine uniforms and then there was some ropey old bird sliding down a pole.

I got a round of cocktails in and made everyone use their willy straws, then I gave Gemma her set of ten tasks for the night. You know, like pinch a short man's bum or kiss a man with a hairy chest. This is what I call 'Forced Fun', when you do what you're meant to do on a hen do but no one is feeling it. The drink wasn't even touching the sides. I knew what would liven this lot up, so I found a group of stags by the bar and brought them over. They were from Romford but I didn't hold that against them. Linda was dirty-dancing with a young bloke within five minutes. It was completely rank and I might as well have been on holiday with Cheryl and Sue.

The girls were having a whale of time with these blokes, but I knew I'd picked badly when I started chatting to one of them. I forget his name so let's call him Gary. For me, talking about prostitutes you've haggled with is a private matter. That's just my personal feeling. I realized Gary was a genuine idiot who thought he was a stand-up comedian when he told me he'd approached a hooker in a red dress the evening before and this had been their conversation:

GARY: So, how much then?

PROSSIE: For what?

GARY: Whatever you want.

PROSSIE: One hour sexy time.

GARY: How much?

PROSSIE: One thousand euros.

GARY: That's not enough.

PROSSIE: What?

GARY: I said that's not enough.

PROSSIE: Twelve hundred euros.

GARY: That's still not enough.

PROSSIE: Two thousand euros.

GARY: OK, that seems fair. But I want the money first.

You see the hilarious thing he did there? This is typical Essex wide-boy humour. And then he told me he actually got her down to €500, so she got his business in the end. Seriously, I'm not joking. He gave me that information. Then he asked me my most dreaded question in the world: 'So what do you do?' It shows you have no imagination if you're asking a girl what she does for a living.

'I'm an actress,' I lied.

'Oh yeah, what you been in?'

'*EastEnders*? I played Michelle Fowler's daughter Vicki in the early days.' That's my favourite lie of all time because people can't challenge it and they're always well impressed. I could see he was gagging for me to ask him back, so I said, 'And what do you do, then?'

'I'm a plumber,' he replied. At least he was honest, but it didn't stop there. 'I wanted to be a gynaecologist because it sounded like a proper mint job. But then I thought, hold up, those birds are there for a reason. They'll be all the manky old ones with maggots dropping out of them. So that's why I became a plumber instead.'

I swear this bloke had practised these 'jokes' in front of a mirror. It was well tragic. I actually couldn't talk to him any longer so I told him I was going for a smoke.

Outside I did see a prostitute in a red dress, but that could have been another hen do. I did think, if that is her, what a shitty life having to shag plums like Gary. I had to ponce a fag off someone because I only smoke when depressed. I think being back in a marina environment just reminded me of Monaco, especially since I wasn't getting on any yachts this time. I'd properly taken that lifestyle for granted, and now I was in a dive full of ugly people. Bastard HQ had shown me the high life to make the low life that much more painful. Although the good news was that everyone else was plastered, even Emily, so they were all fine.

But don't worry, salvation was just around the corner in Antonio Banderas Square (it's seriously called that). As soon as we entered this club called TIBU, I felt right at home. So this was where all the fit blokes had been hiding! My faith restored, I decided I had to get involved in this whole hen do thing. I think I've got some sort of allergy to ugly surroundings and ugly people so that's why I was struggling before. TIBU had a much more sophisticated vibe going on. All you need is swathes of white material in a club and you've Essexed it up. And it had a roof terrace – that's all I ever ask of a place.

As I danced on a table with a glass of champagne in my hand with all the girls surrounding me, I knew I'd finally arrived in Puerto Banus. I know it was Gem's hen do, but it wasn't going to be any good unless I was on top form, was it?

14

champagne: The Lifeblood of Essex

I love waking up because it means the horrors of the previous day are a distant memory. I was completely psyched for what lay ahead: the famous Ocean Club Champagne Spray Party and after-party at Funky Buddha. Personally, this was the main event for me. I'd humoured Gem with the whole dressing-up thing, but this was where the luxury started. We grabbed our bikinis and were out that skuzzy little flat faster than you can say Veuve Clicquot.

It's all about the beach clubs in Marbs, but you got to pay the price if you want to have a good time. The Ocean Club was €3,000 for a giant VIP sunbed between us and a bottle of champagne each, but if you think about it, that means only good-looking, rich people can get into these events.

The *TOWIE* lot seemed to have spent their summer at the new place, Sisu Boutique, but I like to keep it old school, and since I was the one who booked it all, I chose the location. Katie Price and some boyfriend were at the Ocean Club the month before us, so it attracts the names. And wherever the celebs go, that's where the beautiful people go.

At noon we took up our residency by the pool, where we'd be spending the next eight hours sunbathing, dancing and spraying champagne on each other. I'll let you into a secret, though. I've never sprayed champagne on anyone in my life. I actually get quite upset at the thought of abusing these bottles of Veuve when I should be drinking it. So what I do is let people spray me and I usually find there's a lot of takers. As long as I'm not the one shaking the bottle up, I love being covered in expensive champagne.

It was while we were lying by the pool that there was a small incident between me and Brooke. Maybe all the excesses of the party had gone to Brooke's head, but she actually started talking to me about her and Charlie. At first I was pretty receptive and glad she was confiding in me.

'It's just that I hadn't really looked at him in that way before . . . because of you,' she started off. 'But then once it was happening, it made perfect sense. You don't hate me, do you?'

'Of course I don't,' I said. 'I won't lie, I was pretty

239

shocked when Gem told me, but if you're having a good time together, I can't stand in your way. He's a different bloke now – he's off the steroids and he needs someone in his life too.'

Those weren't my true feelings, but what else are you meant to say? That's my ex-boyfriend so I own him for life?

'And it sort of makes more sense,' she went on, 'because I'm short, so he's taller than me. Whereas you were two inches taller in heels, so it looked a bit funny,' she said, ignoring the fact that me and Charlie were the same height when I didn't wear heels. It's no different to what Katie Holmes has to deal with being married to Tom Cruise. I just had to stoop in stilettos. 'I feel so lucky that I found him after all the shitty blokes I've had to put up with.'

'That's true enough. It's all about building up self-respect. Before you know it there'll be blokes queuing up to take you out nice places and treat you properly.'

'You mean like blokes do with you?'

'Well, I have a good time, so I don't see why not.'

'Except I don't want any other blokes now. I just want Charlie,' she said. I tried to say something back but nothing came out. 'You alright?' she said, lifting up her shades to look at me properly.

'Yeah, why wouldn't I be,' I replied, regaining my composure. 'So it's not just a summer fling then?'

'I thought it was, but it's become something else. I

know I'm not the soppy type, but I feel like I've become a lot softer as a person. And that's down to Charlie. Like, we can just look at each other for ages without saying anything and I'll still feel comfortable. And when I curl up into him in bed he tells me we're a snug fit. How sweet is that? I think he's the most attentive bloke I've ever been with. I've honestly never had so much good sex before. I mean, Charlie gets turned on very easily, doesn't he?'

'You what?'

'Didn't you find that, or is it just me?' she said.

I'm sorry, but that's just rude. Just as she was about to start speaking again, I reached into my glass of fizz and flicked it in her face. Right in the eyes.

'Oh my God, what did you do that for? That fucking hurts, you bitch,' she said, rubbing at her eye. 'I'm going to have to take my lenses out now.' And with that she got up and stood right on her champagne flute. It had been a childish tactic to stop her blabbing, but I never wanted shards of glass to get lodged in her foot. She looked down and went completely hysterical on me.

'Oh my God, Brooke, I'm so sorry,' I said repeatedly. Cleo went to get help and before we knew it Brooke was hobbling off with paramedics to get treated. It's bad when a small gesture escalates like that. I felt pretty awful, but I can't help it if Brooke lacks a sensitivity gene. It was bang out of order making me listen to all that.

I was treated like the bad guy all afternoon. Even though I rescued a couple of bottles of champagne from potential sprayers, everyone was well off with me, so I just hung out with other people, mainly blokes, who did have time for me.

Ryan cornered me at the bar later and went, 'Why did you do it, hun?'

'Because there's a lot of fish to fry out there, but she chose my fish,' I said, not making any sense. I tried again. 'Out of all the men in the world, why's she had to go for Charlie? I'm meant to be all supportive to her, but at the end of the day, it's a major betrayal in our friendship. And who's supporting me in all this? It feels like she doesn't care about my feelings so long as she's bagged herself a boyfriend.'

'That's true, but she's not done anything any differently to what you'd do, yeah?' said Ryan. 'Like you always say, you've got to chase whatever makes you happy, and Charlie is that for Brooke.'

'I never say that.'

'You do all the time. You're all like, screw the consequences and look after number one.'

'Hmmm, I talk a lot of toot though, hun,' I replied. 'It would just be nice to know that people were on my side too. I mean, it's blatantly wrong to go out with your best friend's ex. I don't make the rules, that's just how it is.'

'I reckon you need to get a little more honest with

yourself instead of putting on a big front, yeah? Because we always think you're fine with everything, but it's like you're bubbling away and then you explode. It's disturbing.'

'Fine, I will start saying it as I see it,' I said. 'First off, your pants are so tight I can see the outline of your dick. That's disturbing. Secondly, I'm not ready to say sorry to Brooke yet, so don't make me. I'll do it in my own time.'

'Just so long as you don't make the rest of the hen do weird, yeah?' he said as he turned and jumped into the pool.

I didn't want our spat to affect the others either, but I really couldn't promise anything.

※

Understandably, Brooke was sulking and wouldn't talk to me the rest of the day, but to make matters worse, Karen and Paula were moaning about how much money we'd spent already. They should have counted themselves lucky because I heard they were charging £500 to go to Sisu Boutique's TOWIE pool party. Why would you pay to see the cast when you can see them for free on Loughton High Street? The thing was, I was showing them the Marbs jet-set lifestyle at a fraction of the price. When they were going on at me I said, 'Are we or are we not having fun at the Ocean Club?', and they admitted they were loving it. Having a good time doesn't come for free, you know.

Shame they hadn't managed to look the part too. Fair enough, they couldn't have gotten away with my denim hot pants, but it was like they were sabotaging their own tans. Karen had been wearing a swimsuit that I can only describe as a harness. She had so many straps going everywhere that by the end of the day she looked like a pork chop fresh off the griddle. And that's another thing: why don't people apply suntan lotion properly or reapply? When I see sunburn, I actually fill up with rage. It's ugly and there's no need. Ryan is a serial offender, but he always goes, 'Nah, just you wait, I'll be a lovely golden brown tomorrow, yeah?' To be fair that does happen, but if he went higher than SPF4, he'd bypass the red stage. I just don't get it.

I'd even done a bit of networking for the girls while I was meant to be chilling in the pool. These two Irish blokes were going to Funky Buddha later too, and they knew the promoter. Not only were they going to get us in for free, they would try and get us into VIP. That's all I ever ask of life.

By the time 6 o'clock rolled round I'd properly sobered up again, which was good news because we needed to get back and get ready for the evening's entertainment and I can't do my make-up drunk. I was sure I'd told everyone that Sunday night was white-themed, but once again Karen and Paula hadn't got the memo and came out their bedroom in black. What gives? No matter – I'm not precious about these things and Gemma didn't care as long as she was having the night of her life. I'll admit I'd broken my own dress code by wearing tiny sparkly black shorts, but I put a white kaftan over, which just about skimmed them, and wore my new Gucci gun-metal-grey python sandals.

I'd got inspired by Lydia Bright at the polo. In my opinion, she's got the best style out of all the girls because she's obsessed with Sarah Jessica Parker. It makes her a bit more daring in her choices. I was beside myself when I found out Lydia's shop Bella Sorella was just down the road from me in Loughton. Jessica Wright has her lingerie shop there too, but in my opinion it looks so out of place. Look out for the candy-coloured shop front sandwiched between the shabby bookshop and a crusty old newsagent's. Loughton High Road is hardly Fifth Avenue, but I will say one thing in its favour. Every WEG dreams of having her own boutique, so there's not as much room for chains on the high street. I honestly reckon that's the reason why West Essex has such a unique sense of style.

I'd been plying the girls and boy with cava the whole three hours we'd been getting ready because I'd been forced to make a decision that would get a mixed reaction. We were meant to eat at a PB institution, La Pappardella. You can't go wrong with Italian if you need to line your stomach. But since I was cost-cutting, I cancelled that and took them all to Burger King. Oh my God, there was uproar. I tried to explain to these girls that eating out would totally zap our drinking money, but it really hadn't sunk in that PB was about to get a whole lot more expensive. Brooke had a go at me for not booking dinner in the club, but that just showed what an amateur she was. If you go eat at a club's restaurant, you're just asking for aloof service and pricey menus. I want that in a club, but I don't want that from my restaurant experience too.

So the bottom line was, I couldn't enjoy my Whopper in peace because everyone had something to say. I mean, do I look like a holiday rep? Ryan was on my side, but Karen and Paula didn't even back me up or thank me for budgeting. I will never diss the Chancellor of the Exchequer again because no one ever recognizes that spending cuts are for everyone's benefit in the long-run. But here's my advice to him – if you're getting grief on *Question Time*, just get everyone down the karaoke fast. They soon forget their gripes when you whack on some Dolly Parton.

I'd reserved us a table in O'Grady's, which is nothing fancy, just pure fun. It must be the only Irish bar in the world nestled between Burger King and Louis Vuitton. That's PB for you. I've got to say, I'm a bit of a pro when it comes to this singing lark. I'm not saying I'm any good, but it's in my blood. Whenever we used to come to PB as a family back in the day, Dad would always drag us to one of those sophisticated places on the water-front that I mentioned. Not that he's any good either.

'Mack the Knife' is his only song and he talks it rather than sings it. I've also dabbled in a bit of singing and dancing at the Fox Family's other Spanish retreat in La Manga. In the Hyatt's infamous Piano Bar you'll find the legend that is Brian Chapman the Piano Man. You just write down your request and then he'll tinkle out Billy Joel and Elton John classics. That's my cue to climb up on the piano and dance, but you can only get three girls up there max. I realize this is turning in to a running theme, but it's more fun dancing up high. Just saying. Although last time I was there, they'd banned piano dancing. Maybe someone had fallen off and spoilt it for everyone. Anyways, if you convince Brian that you're a good enough singer, he'll let you belt one out. I'm all for audience participation as long as it's not bleeding 'Mack the Knife'.

Dad actually bought a place out there over ten years ago. It's got its own pool, which is where you'll find me and the girls for a good eight hours. The sun's got to be different out there because I've never seen myself looking so brown. I mean, you really only go to La Manga for the sun, golf or hotel bars. It's a middle-aged man's paradise. But the Hyatt is home to some proper scandals, like when the Leicester City team got accused of gang-banging, not to mention the Paul Gascoigne room-trashing incident and the Rio Ferdinand fight-over-a-pool-table brawl. And Dad was fuming when he got caught in Stan Collymore's fire extinguisher explosion in the Piano Bar. If I'm to be honest, I've done some really bad things there too, but what goes on in La Manga stays in La Manga. The heat can make you do crazy things.

Naturally, I was first up on the karaoke. I'm all about the show tunes and you cannot go wrong with 'Copacabana'. The thing about that one is that it's a story-song, so even if you're shit, everyone wants to know what's going to happen to Lola the showgirl. Never fails. I was made to sing the second song too as there were still no takers. Can I just say, don't try singing Rihanna's 'Rude Boy'. I honestly didn't realize how graphic the lyrics were, but once I started I had to commit. Gem's mum was open-mouthed throughout. I suppose it was a leap from Barry Manilow.

Cleo forced herself to sing Katy Perry just to get me off the mic. As she started singing, I spotted Ryan leave the bar. I assumed he'd gone out for a fag, but when he hadn't returned after thirty minutes, I decided I had to track him down. I couldn't believe my eyes when I found him. There he was sat at a table outside La Pappardella with a huge bowl of creamy Carbonara and a lovely glass of red wine.

'Oh I see, I see, having a posh dinner for one, are we?' I said.

'Oh my God, how did you find me?'

'Hun, you're never far behind an Italian waiter. What you playing at?'

'I didn't want a dirty burger. My body's a temple, yeah? And it needs proper fuel.'

'But why did you say you were happy going to Burger King?'

'Yeah, I was happy for all you lot to go there, just had my own plans. Didn't want to tempt anyone to overspend, did I?' he replied.

'Give me a mouthful and I won't tell anyone,' I said, taking two huge mouthfuls. Is there anything nicer than cream, mushrooms and fettucine when you're drunk? As I went in for a third, Ryan grabbed the fork off me.

'Oi, leave off,' he protested. 'You've had your Whopper and you gotta deal with that now, yeah?'

God, I was well jel at Ryan's ingenuity. If I hadn't been in charge of this sham of a hen do, I'd have been sat there myself.

'Well hurry up then, because we got the special entertainment coming up,' I said, winking at Ryan. I then called the waiter over for a cold glass of Prosecco. If you can't beat them, join them.

By the time we got back, Gem's mum Linda was lining up a load of shots at the bar for all the girls and the bar staff. It was green so I didn't like to ask, we just got involved. Brooke was in charge of the entertainment, and when he arrived, I was proper disappointed. We'd requested a hot policeman, but instead we'd been given a member of the puberty police. I swear he was only eighteen and the skinniest little thing with spiky blond hair. Since me and Brooke still weren't talking I couldn't say anything, but I heard Ryan go to her, 'Hun, I can't watch this,' and he's always up for people taking their clothes off.

This kid did all the classic stripper banter with Gem like, 'I hear you've been a very bad girl and I'm going to teach you a lesson you won't forget,' but it's not so convincing when someone's voice hasn't broken. It started off tame enough, just some really horrible dance routine to some bad Euro beats. The more full on it got, the more Linda was loving it. I mean, she was actually cheering on this hairless child as he struggled to pin her daughter to the floor before gyrating up and down her. He had rhythm though, I'll give him that.

I could see Gem was trying look like she was having a laugh but the frozen smile said it all. By the time he told her to get up against the wall and 'spread 'em', Gem was obeying orders just to get it over and done with. As he thrust back and forth behind her, Linda grabbed hold of him from behind and joined in. You know that film *The Human Centipede?* This was way more disturbing to watch. All the girls had their hands over their mouths except for Emily who was shielding her eyes. Ryan seemed to have changed his tune, since he was stood there filming the whole thing and cackling. And we hadn't even got to the worst bit.

Once the stripper was down to his pants, he pushed her onto a chair, aimed baby oil down her cleavage and actually stuck his hand down her top. I'm no expert on strippers but isn't that some sort of violation? Gem's smile didn't fade and she just pulled his hand out. She must have been traumatized because to this day she won't let us joke about it. She also made Ryan delete the footage from his iPhone and YouTube, which was fair enough.

As if things couldn't get any more graphic, he then threatened to whip his jockeys off. I'd said to Brooke when she was booking the stripper, don't pay extra for the full monty, but the girl can't do things by halves. The moment that kid walked in I could see Brooke wanted her €20 back.

Turns out the grand finale was the only sight worth paying for. I can honestly say, each one of us went into a state of hysteria as soon as them pants landed in Gem's face. He may have had a baby-face up top but down below he had a baby's arm. This man-child totally messed with my mind but I didn't question his stripper credentials after that. How the kid had the strength to lug that thing around, I do not know.

Linda was still trying to molest him afterwards as he went about finding his clothes. This is exactly why mums shouldn't be allowed on hen dos. They're completely unmanageable.

I saw Brooke was still reeling with delight after the entertainment. I thought now's as good a time as any to clear the air and went over to her.

'Oh my God, where the hell did you find that police-boy?' I said. She stopped laughing and just glared at me. 'How's the foot?' I said, trying again.

'It's pretty painful, if you must know,' she replied.

'Should you be wearing heels?'

'It's only the back of my foot,' she said, still giving nothing back.

'You know I didn't mean that to happen, don't you?' I said, 'It's like BHQ planted that glass there or something. The last thing I'd ever want to do is hurt you.' I couldn't quite manage an apology because I still thought she'd been out of order. She turned and hobbled off back to our reserved area. Gemma had been watching the whole thing and came over to console.

'You alright, babe?'

'I've fucked up, Gem. What am I going to do?'

'You two are like a married couple sometimes. You got a lot of love, but you don't half know how to wind each other up. She can't stay mad at you for long.'

I don't know why but I started getting really upset. Gem just wasn't getting how cut-up I was about all this. Like Ryan said, I'm always smiling through gritted teeth, which leads to embarrassing explosions. Unfortunately, this one was worse than most.

'I don't want to lose her,' I suddenly found myself wailing. 'Everyone's moving on without me.'

People were starting to look at me like I was Susan Boyle having a full-on tantrum.

'Shhh, babe, no one's going nowhere,' said Ryan, who looked like he wanted to put a comforting hand over my mouth.

'Why's everyone so obsessed with settling down anyway? You're all boys' girls and you can't even see it,' I wailed. 'Worth throwing away your friendships for a bloke, is it? I mean, you can get married, but ten years down the line with sprogs hanging off your droopy boobs, you'll all be gagging to be with your girlfriends and you won't have none. One in three marriages fail anyway.' I couldn't stop mouthing off and now Gemma was crying. I was like a hen do assassin, shooting down friends one by one.

'What's your problem, Becs,' Gemma said finally. 'Are you saying you're going to carry on going out with flash, arrogant pricks just because they show you a good time? If anyone's a boy's girl, it's you.'

'Oh, I see, *et tu*, Judas?' I screamed. 'Why not have a few more stabs while you're at it.'

'I'll hit you with one,' said Brooke, only too eager to talk to me now. 'You broke Charlie's heart so I really don't get what my big crime is in all this. You didn't want him no more, hun. With respect, you need to let him move on.'

'With respect, Brooke, you need to remember he's my ex and we got history. You can't expect me to shut it down just because you're doing him. It's like you don't have the facility to feel other people's pain. You're the only girl I know who never cried during *The Notebook*. That's just weird. Even I managed to do that much.'

'They're fucking acting,' Brooke yelled just at the moment the music cut out.

One of the bar staff grabbed the microphone and turned to all of us. 'I hope you've all been having a laugh tonight, people. So it's our final karaoke song of the night and the hen has requested that Brooke, Becci and Ryan join her in a Take That classic, "Everything Changes". Take it away, ladies.'

By this point we were all in bits, even Ryan. He gets set off when he see others crying like it's contagious. Gemma wiped her face, took a deep breath and grabbed that mic. If she was doing it, then we all had to. Have you ever seen people sobbing as they sing an upbeat song? It ruins the song for ever, and whenever I hear it now, I just feel sick. We had mascara running down our faces and I'd probably gone bright red because that's what happens. I'm not an attractive crier and I was properly shaking. That didn't seem to stop Linda happily snapping away at us. I couldn't work out if she was oblivious or an opportunist. I sang the line 'Everything changes but you' so many times that eventually I doubled over because it was all too painful.

When the music finally stopped, the DJ quickly put on some loud music to cover the deafening silence. Let's just say if this had been *The X Factor*, we'd have been the freaks they get back for the final show.

Just to make matters worse, the night was still young. Our next venue to bring down was Funky Buddha, so I had to call one of the Irish guys to say we were on our way. I mean, we were on the guest list, but remember that's not VIP, yeah? Problem was I'd properly killed the mood. Since I'd lost my audience I had to ask Cleo to take the lead, but I told her exactly what to say. And I gave her money for a round of shots before we left. It was important to get everyone tanked up, and I desperately needed to take the edge off the night.

I honestly think I was having some sort of quarter-life crisis because I'm not normally this loopy. Swear to God, it's not my style to make scenes and insult the bride-to-be. I wasn't proud of myself, that's for sure.

Once we'd all sorted ourselves and fixed our make-up, Cleo led the way to the taxis. I could have made life easy for myself and got us on the guest list at Pangea which is right in PB, but it's not a super-club in my view. It's nice because it's open-air, but it's not as upmarket as Funky Buddha and the prices represent that. Although getting into Funky Buddha wasn't as easy as I'd hoped either. I hadn't really told the Irish boys there were nine of us and the door bitch was having none of it, so we had to split into two groups and my lot got in first, but that meant we had to do all the hard work to get into VIP.

Just to put this place into perspective, people had paid €120 to see 50 Cent just two weeks earlier. And it totally kicked off because people thought he was going to perform, but he just sat in VIP and sprayed the crowd with champagne. Who does he think he is? Anyways, there were no names this night so I thought getting in would be a breeze, but then again, I had Cleo, Gemma, Karen and their mum with me.

I marched up to this guy stood next to the bouncer and I went, 'Are you the promoter?' and he said he was, so I said, 'We're mates of Ciaran's and he said you could get us in.'

'Did he now? What's in it for me?' replied the guy.

'Depends what you're after,' I said, trying to be as elusive as him.

'Why don't you and her kiss for me,' he said, pointing at Cleo. 'With tongues, for one minute.'

We'd done much worse before just for a free drink so this was a piece of piss. I knew Cleo would be up for it so I negotiated our way past the rope before giving him a serious show. He clapped like a bloody monkey at the end. Because men's cocks do most of the thinking, this makes them pretty simple. And that's why women will always have the upper hand. I mean, who's really more powerful, Simon Cowell or his ex-girlfriends? Yeah, you know it. Can you honestly imagine a woman putting her past flings on the payroll? Just wouldn't happen because we use our noggins.

Once we were in, this promoter guy flagged over a waitress to bring extra flutes. That's what I'm talking about. Just as I thought the party was getting started, I spotted Ryan, Brooke, Paula and Emily walking in, so I said to the guy, 'Can our friends come in too?' He replied, 'I don't know why you're asking me, I don't work here.' Turned out he was a promoter, just not a promoter for Funky Buddha. It was a cheap trick but I can't get mad at a fellow chancer. The problem was even Ciaran and his mate couldn't get in because the real promoter hadn't shown up yet. It was a bit of a moral dilemma, but after all that had happened that evening, I knew in my heart that we should leave. After all, it was all about partying together, and, to be honest, it's such a nice club it doesn't matter if you're not in VIP. Unless that's where all the talent is. Reluctantly, we trailed out. I gave the bouncer a mournful look and he avoided eye contact, the coward. He knew he would crumble.

Loads of places in Marbs seem to be Asian-inspired, and that's why a lot of Essex places have nicked the theme. You just need to look at all the Thai statues in Sugar Hut to see this. But since I got an interior designer for a mother, I think I can say this with all authority: the places in Marbs think they're making it Asian but the end result always looks Moroccan. I suppose Morocco's across the water, and if they get Moroccan builders in then the end result is going to be Moroccan. I'm not complaining, just saying.

The boys had a reserved table so we joined them and got a hookah brought over. So Moroccan. A while later that promoter bloke came over to me and went, 'I'm sorry, love, but I couldn't resist earlier. You lot were fine, but they're proper strict on big groups coming in.'

'Well, I hope it gave you a good laugh and a stiffy. Anyways, no harm done and, to be honest, Cleo's a good kisser so everyone's a winner,' I replied.

'I like a girl who doesn't take life too seriously,' he laughed. Clearly he hadn't realized I was a ticking time-bomb of hormones just waiting to go off again. He then said, 'I think I owe you, so can I buy you ladies a drink?'

'I thought you'd never ask. How about a glass of champagne each?' I replied.

'Coming right up,' he said without even flinching.

I don't know if I've got the message across yet, but you just *cannot* buy more than one drink for yourself in a club round here. I'm not joking, it's €40 just for a glass of fizz. I'll do the maths for you: nine glasses would have cost him €360, but he actually got us two bottles of Moet Rosé for €400 all in. Maybe he got more for his money, who can say? But you know in Essex how getting blokes to buy you a drink is all part of the social game? Here it's a necessity. The thing is, these blokes *want* to be seen buying drinks, and I want to be the person they're buying them for. I've got money so I could buy them if I wanted, but why would I do that when some guy gets off on looking the Big Shot? The only reason Puerto Banus gets away with charging those prices is because there are mugs paying them. And the good news is Marbs is riddled with them, so everyone's happy.

The promoter, who was called Brad, returned to our table with some blonde in tow. I totally loved the girl the moment she started talking. She was a bit goofy and she called everyone 'bubbla', but she was so down-to-earth and she had the most infectious laugh ever. I was in hysterics the whole time she was talking. It turned out she was Brad's sister Lauren. I don't know what happened in Essex in the Eighties, but I swear it's the most common girls' name. I mean, I know twenty Laurens on Facebook alone and then there's those two in *TOWIE*. So I said to this Lauren, why so many? And she goes, 'Well, my mum loved Ralph Lauren clothes so I was going to be Ralph if I was a boy and Lauren if I was a girl.'

'Are you serious?' I said.

'A hundred per cent. And she also loves Yves Saint Laurent, which is just the French version, so that done it for her.'

'Fuck, I'm glad my mum didn't do that or I'd be called Burberry. Burberry Fox.'

'Oh my God, I fucking love it! Bubbla, I'm totally christening you that.' She dabbed her fingers in the champagne and slapped them on my forehead. I felt like a new woman and we downed the rest in one.

'So where you guys staying anyway?' I asked.

'Sisu Hotel. Or *TOWIE* Towers is what Brad calls it,' she said, rolling her eyes.

'They got to be offering them free accommodation. The only way is comp, right?'

'I dunno, bubbla. It's a bit of a coincidence them all being there,' she said, all puzzled. 'Like, Brad knows Mark Wright through promoting clubs out here and they've both been doing stuff for Pangea and TIBU. So that's the only reason Lauren came out. They were proper moody so I was glad to see the back of them, to be honest.'

'God, do those two ever have fun together?' I said. See, I sensed they were wrong for each other even back then.

'I know, right? But I tell you who has been having a laugh,' she said with a glint in her eye. 'Arg and Lydia. He was out here with Mark and he had some gig down Nikki Beach, but he's stayed on and Lydia's flown out to be with him.'

'Oh my God, you're kidding? You serious?' I asked.

'Swear to God, bubbla. I saw them mucking around in the pool yesterday. They're definitely back together.'

'Well, good for them. As long as he don't mess her around again. I'm sorry, but I feel well protective towards old Lyds,' I said to Lauren as she slid off her chair.

I tell you what, there was a lot of bad stuff being said about Arg earlier that year so Lydia was totally right to have given him the shove. Understandably he was suddenly getting all this attention from women who never would've looked at him before. Like if you walk behind him, you'll notice he lollops. Obviously that's endearing, but before *TOWIE* it really wasn't. Nor was the shaved head. But the TV show gave him the same opportunities as Mark, and from what I heard, he explored those opportunities. But what do I know, I didn't see any of this.

You got to be careful with the Essex rumour mill because things can get exaggerated just because people want to look like they're in the know. I mean, Arg's little sister Natasha is a classic example. Someone told me that she was desperate to be in *TOWIE* but the producers wouldn't let her because she's a right chubster. I mean, virtually everyone has shoe-horned a family member in to the show – Mark, Lauren G, Sam, Joey, Amy, Lydia, Kirk – but until Nanny Brighton rocked up one Christmas, we never saw any of Arg's lot. You see, the shunned fat sister story made perfect sense. But then one day Tash made me go down Woodford Wells, which is her local tennis club, because she thought she could beat me. She couldn't. She turns round after losing the first set and goes, 'That's Arg's sister over there.' And keep in mind I was looking out for a young Vanessa Feltz. The girl on the next court was an absolutely stunning blonde, and toned too.

'You don't mean her, do you?' I asked and Tasha says, 'Yeah, the pretty one.'

She's only a bloody tennis coach! How is she going to be a chubster if that's her job? Tasha introduced us later and I said, 'If my sister was in *TOWIE*, I'd be poking my head in all her scenes just to annoy her.' But Arg's sister just said that it was Arg's thing and tennis was hers, plus that wasn't her set of friends so it wouldn't make sense for her to pop up. I won't lie, I liked the girl a lot and she talked a lot of sense. So it just goes to show, the truth is pretty boring sometimes and that's why West Essex must continue to fabricate stories. I honestly live for that shit and I will happily spread the muck too.

Lauren had gone off to the toilets so I searched the group for conversations of interest. It seemed to me that there was some innocent flirting occurring between Brad and a few of the girls. If anyone needed action it was Cleo, so I turned round to her and Brad and went, 'You two would be so good together, you know.'

Cleo gave me proper dagger eyes and went, 'Err, I don't think so,' and then tried to move the conversation on. Seriously, someone had to play cupid. She always moans she never pulls and I keep telling her it's because she plays it too cool. To the point she'll actually look uninterested and avoid all eye contact. What gives? The only reason she did it with that famous comedian was because *he* picked *her*. I knew she wouldn't thank me, but you got to do unpopular things sometimes. So I carried on.

'No, honestly, any girl would be lucky to have you, Brad, and Cleo's an extremely special person. I think you two could do beautiful things together,' I said. You can accuse me of overegging the pudding all you like, but as soon as I'd laid Cleo's cards on the table, I could see a change in Brad. It's like he was seeing Cleo for the first time, and wouldn't you know it, she looked away all demure. But it was fine to do that now because the wheels were in motion.

Brad went, 'So do you fancy me then?' and Cleo replied, 'You're alright,' and rolled her eyes. And Brad just laughed because he knew the chase was on. The dance floor was calling me, so I grabbed Ryan and left them to it.

When we came back to the table, I couldn't tell if any snogging had occurred but I didn't worry as I knew Brad and Lauren weren't going anywhere without us that night. Brad leaned into the group and went, 'Ladies and boy, how about we take this party elsewhere.'

'Depends where you're suggesting,' I said. 'I can't commit until I have the full facts in front of me.'

'Olivia Valere. I do a good job at promoting their nights so I reckon I can get us all into VIP there. More lively, more beautiful, more sexy, what's not to like?'

'How about the fact we'll be in Marbs town,' I said. I know my clubs and we were getting further and further from Puerto Banus. 'Don't get me wrong, I've heard good things about the place, but our hen do is in your hands so we have high expectations, yeah?'

'I've never disappointed a group of women yet,' he said with one hundred per cent confidence. What did we have to lose?

I didn't realize that Brad hadn't been drinking all night because he was driving. He had this slick-looking black Maserati GranCabrio, but unfortunately it was only last year's model. Joking! I love Italian models of all ages.

'Who wants to be my plus-one?' he asked as the valet brought his car round. He was looking at Cleo, but she shoved Gem towards the car and, to be fair, it was the popular choice. We all screamed as she got in and off they sped into the night. I wanted to be excited, but supercars just took me back to Monaco again. You shouldn't feel sadness when looking at supercars and yachts. Bloody Ben.

I distracted myself by sorting out cabs for everyone but made sure I wasn't sharing with Brooke. Gemma had completely brushed off all the mental things I'd said earlier. She's never been one to bear a grudge which is an amazing trait to have, but she must store it all some-where. Brooke, however, made it obvious she was still gunning for me, so I clung to Lauren like she was a human shield.

As our taxi whizzed down the highway to Olivia Valere, I caught a flash of a Maserati on the side of the road next to some flashing blue lights.

'Oh my God, did you see that? The police have stopped Brad and Gem,' I said, practically shaking Lauren who was busy singing to some loud Euro toot on the radio. 'Lauren, did you hear me?'

It's like she had cloth for ears. When we all got out

the taxis, I told everyone in the most animated way possible exactly what I'd seen. We all smelt a palaver brewing.

'What if they caught her giving Brad a blowie?' said Brooke.

'Hun, don't say shit like that in front of Linda,' I said, giving Brooke a verbal slap. Like Linda cared. Staying upright was her main concern by that point.

'You know what it is, bubbla,' slurred Lauren. 'He's only gone and got pulled over for speeding again.'

And she was so right. Fifteen minutes later, Brad and Gem flew into sight. Brad jumped out and threw the keys at the valet. 'Sorry about that, ladies – I had a meeting with a policeman.'

'What's going on?' I asked.

'Got pulled over for doing a poxy one hundred,' said Brad, looking mystified. 'I told the bloke, this car can do two hundred miles an hour and I'm doing half that so I've done you a favour. He weren't having none of it so I got another fine.'

'Weird this always happens when you've got a girl in the passenger seat, right, bubs?' said Lauren, tapping away at her brother like only a sister knows how.

'Shut up, Lozza. What we all doing hanging out in a car park? Let's get involved,' he said, leading the way.

I got to say I was well impressed with the club. It was more Spanish than any place I'd been to and that made it feel instantly more Mediterranean and sexy.

Like everyone just looked proper fit and the whole scene was more sophisticated. As promised, Brad got us all into VIP and our table was lit up with bottles of champagne sparklers. Seriously, did everything in Marbs have to be like Monaco? BHQ must have been having a right laugh at my expense. A glass was shoved in my hand and Gem stood up to make a toast.

'I just wanted to say thank you to all my girls and boy for making this a night to remember. If it weren't for you lot I wouldn't be standing here as the soon-to-be Mrs Sweet. You've kept me sane during the bad times and drunk during the daytimes. So thank you all and God bless,' she said, raising her glass before adding, 'And special thanks to all my bridesmaids for making this trip so memorable and for getting this far without getting sacked.'

Everyone laughed except me because she was blatantly ripping the piss out of my sister. Tasha honestly did fire three of her bridesmaids during her engagement. One of them got the shove after she sent out a stream of emails about the hen do 'timetable' which ensured no room for spontaneity or fun. Who wants to go to a club at 23:00 hours? My sister had it out with her and told her to stop being so bossy and the friend stormed off. So technically she resigned. Then one of them tried it on with Jake so she got kicked out (like being eighteen made him the innocent party). The worst one was the girl she fired the week before the wedding. They got so coked up on a night out that all these harsh truths came out and it turned into a proper catfight. She's never told me what was said but it must have been pretty bad. By the time the wedding day rolled around, I felt privileged to have made it to the final three.

I drank my champagne pretty quickly because now I was in VIP I felt relaxed, and I was on a mission to get wrecked. As I reached to pour myself another glass, a man's hand got the bottle before me.

'Please, allow me,' he said smoothly. This guy was in his mid-forties I'd say, but he looked good for it.

'Well, don't mind if you do,' I replied. 'You sound local, hun.'

'Your hearing is good. I speak Spanish but I'm actually from Argentina,' he said.

'Oh yeah? I've heard it's nice there.' I didn't even know the place so I steered us out of this conversational cul-de-sac and went, 'So how comes you're in VIP?'

'I'm an actor. You wouldn't know me in England but I've got a few fans here,' he said.

'So tell me what you been in,' I said, genuinely interested now.

'You wouldn't have heard of it but it's a really popular show here in Spain. It's about four men who are called in to help regular people out of tricky situations. For instance, in one episode, an artist is bullied and ripped off by a powerful art dealer and the team assist the artist . . .'

'Can I stop you right there, babe. This sounds just like *The A-Team*,' I said.

'Sorry, what team?'

'You know, B.A., Hannibal. There was a film about them too. You know, if you have a problem and no one else can help?'

He wasn't getting it. The cultural barrier was making it such hard work. I suddenly felt this urge to kiss him just to end the confusion. So I did, but I got way more than I bargained for. This man seriously put every Essex boy in the shade. It was like proper urgent kissing and I could genuinely tell that we'd have the most incredible sex. He was definitely attractive, but because he hadn't been all arrogant and try-hard, I hadn't really been flirting with him. I'm obviously too conditioned to mouthy Essex blokes to even recognize true suaveness when it's before me. He was lovely looking for an older man as well. I can only describe him as Don Draper's more tanned and handsome twin brother.

'Can I get you another drink,' the actor said to me. I just nodded in case my words ruined the moment. 'I'll get the waitress to come over. Excuse me, I must go to the bathroom,' he said, leaving.

Gemma and Ryan were straight on me the moment he walked off. 'Oh my God, he is so hot,' said Gem.

'Like he could be your dad but a fit dad, yeah?' said Ryan.

'Shut up. He's only . . . well, maybe if my dad had had

me at sixteen, then yeah. Young blokes could learn a trick or two off that bloke,' I said.

'What's his name?' asked Ryan.

'Who needs names when you got passion?' I said before screaming, 'Oh my God, you guys, look at Cleo!'

There was my girl snogging the face off Brad. I told you my blatant tactics would pay off. I'm telling you, a lot of single girls could do with a friend like me.

When I turned back round, Gemma and Ryan had jumped up on the sofa to dance. I took no persuading and we joined them as quick as a flash. It was exhilarating and I just felt a lot of love for her and Ryan at that precise moment. When you've known people since you were eleven years old, there's nothing you don't know about each other. Gem turned to me and went, 'I'm having the best night of my life,' and gave me the biggest hug. 'Don't ever go changing because I have more fun with you than anyone else. You're honestly the only person that makes me cry with laughter.'

'Awww, babe. We are pretty fucking funny. Remember our butt-buffing dance?' I said, gearing up.

'Oh my God, like, only the hottest dance ever invented in 2002 . . . Bring it, hun.' And with that command we butt-buffed our little hearts out.

It's not a complicated manoeuvre – you just lift your arms in the air and bounce your butts off each other in time to the music but real sexy and slow. It's hot. And you have to turn as you're doing it so you'll side butt-buff each other, or sometimes do a proper back-to-back butt-buff. The options are endless. Anyways, me and Gemma had got a real rhythm going on up on that sofa. All eyes were on us and we were in our element. Gem leaned into me as we front-buffed and went, 'Still got it, hun.'

To show my solidarity, I gave her a real hard butt-buff. Instead of standing strong as I thought she would, she went flying. I reached out to pull her back but it was too late. She landed on the ground with a thud that was louder than the beat in the club. I honestly couldn't move from the sofa and nor did anyone else. Why was BHQ so intent on making me damage my friends? She didn't move either, and the only thought that went through my head was, 'I promise never to butt-buff another person so long as I live.'

15

The Science of Sunning It

'Oh my God, Gem, I'm so sorry. You alright?' I said finally, climbing down to her side.

'Yeah, fine. I just fell funny. I think I winded myself,' Gem replied, gasping.

'Do you want us to pick you up?'

'Yeah, that would be nice,' she winced. So me and Ryan took an armpit each and heaved her onto the sofa. She yelped so bad I thought I'd done her more damage.

'What is it?' I said. She didn't seem to be bleeding and I couldn't work out where she was hurting.

'I fell on my hand. I think I've sprained it,' she said.

'Ryan, why don't you get some ice and I'll take a closer look,' I said. See, I told you I was calm in a crisis. Once I'd dispatched Ryan I examined her hand, which was resting on her belly.

'Looks fine to me, hun. It doesn't look swollen at all,'

I said, feeling a wash of relief. The colour had even returned to her cheeks.

'Thank fuck! Maybe if I just sit here for a bit and get that ice on it, it'll calm down,' she replied.

'Oh my days, I'm proper shaking, Gem. A butt-buff has never ended in physical violence before. Maybe we haven't got it in us any more. Maybe we're too old for dance routines,' I said. Gemma just glared at me and went, 'Shut. Up,' and shook her head in disgust.

I left her and Ryan to it because the actor was back and I needed to calm my nerves. Seriously, he was pure man. I just wanted to tear right into him. I tried to tell him about the trauma that had happened in his absence, but he looked blankly at me. I gave up and we just started kissing furiously again. I suppose this is how you make relationships work if you're from different countries. You know, the language of love and all that.

After a while, I felt a tap on my shoulder. I turned round to find Brooke standing there.

'Yeah, what is it?' I said coldly.

'Gem's not feeling good so she wants to go back to the apartment. I thought you might want to too, seeing as you're the one who butt-buffed her.'

'It was an accident. And I'm sort of busy,' I replied.

'Suit yourself. I'm sure she won't be upset.' The bitch was emotionally playing me.

'Fine, we'll call it a night. I'm honestly not bothered,'

I said. I was so angry because she had completely done that on purpose and it's not like I was going to let the bride go home alone and injured. The actor said he sometimes came to the UK so we swopped numbers. You never know, right? Then obviously I swopped numbers with my new best friend Lauren and I made sure Brooke saw. Displaced already.

Gem kept the ice pack on as we walked out. She'd gone proper pale again. As we left, I realized the rest of the group wasn't with us. 'Why we leaving them all behind?' I asked. And Brooke replied, 'No point in ending everyone's evening.'

Oh my God, I was so mad with her. She'd singled me out and clit-blocked me out of pure spite. I said nothing and just kept a lid on it. We sat either side of Gem in the cab but you could cut the tension with a nail file.

'God, it fucking hurts,' Gem gasped suddenly. 'I don't think I can take it any more.'

'Take the ice pack off and let me have a look, will you?' said Brooke. Her reaction was the total opposite of mine. 'Fucking hell, Gem. Your wrist is all bent out of shape. Why's it all puffed up like that?'

'Babe, don't scare the girl. It looks fine,' I said.

'Are you blind? Shit, we need to go to a hospital,' Brooke said in full-on panic mode.

'I'll be fine once I've slept it off,' said Gem.

'Oi, *señor*, take us to the hospital. *La hospital, pronto*,' Brooke shouted.

'Oh my God, you're totally overreacting,' I said. 'I'm looking at it now and it looks the same as my hand.'

'Just trust me, yeah?'

I had no choice but to become part of Brooke's drama. Gemma started crying so hard that even I felt a bit scared now.

A&E was shockingly quiet compared to my local. Whipps Cross is like the night of the living dead at 3 a.m. on a weekend. You can't move for bloodied limbs. Incidentally, great people have been born in that hospital. Me, James Argent, David Beckham, Jonathan Ross, to name but a few legends. Anyways, as they took Gem behind some curtains, one of the nurses goes to me, 'What caused this?' I thought about it and said, 'I would have to say alcohol.' She just tutted and walked off. Charming! What was I meant to say? My left buttock?

It turned into one of the most traumatic nights of my life. They said she'd broken her wrist in multiple places and they'd have to work on it right now. After dosing her up on morphine, they plunged a syringe into her hand to draw out the blood that was causing the swelling. If that wasn't excruciating enough, we stood by her as they manipulated her wrist back into position. Gem's cries went straight through me. I can still hear them now. I wouldn't have wished this kind of thing on my worst enemy, not even Bucket. By the end, we were all sobbing like we'd given birth. Gem had been on the gas and air throughout, but the doctor thought it best if we all took a lungful. Can I just say, they should sell that stuff outside clubs. I'd felt a hangover coming on in the hospital, but as soon as I breathed that shit in, I felt amazing, although it made our voices go really deep which was an unattractive side effect.

After they'd bandaged Gem up, they wheeled her off to get some sleep. There was nothing for it but to head back to the apartment and do the same ourselves.

I never thought I could hate glaring sunshine but it was the last thing I needed. As we stood waiting for our cab, I thought about the massive ordeal Brooke and I had been through in the last four hours. Having this shared experience pushed me to saying something to her. Something that showed I appreciated her.

'Babe, I'm so glad you made us come here. If it had just been me and Gem, she'd be sleeping with a bent wrist in our filthy room right now.'

'I knew in my gut it was serious,' she replied.

'Can I make a confession?' I said.

'Yeah, go on.'

'I was looking at the wrong wrist the whole time,' I said. Brooke's eyes were wide open now. 'I was looking at her right wrist instead of her left and that did look fine, so I was semi-right.'

'Oh my God, you dozy mare. Good job you didn't take up that medical degree,' she said scornfully. 'At what point did you realize?'

'About thirty minutes ago when they were wrapping

her arm up. The hand I looked at earlier had no ring on, and then I thought, funny, somebody's put a ring on it now.'

'Shit, what's going to happen with the wedding now?' she asked.

'Babe, I can't even go there mentally right now,' I replied wearily. 'But what I do know is that Linda is going to be well pissed off. Not that it's our fault. I mean, she was so off her tits she didn't even notice any of this going on, so she can't talk.'

We stood in silence again. I knew this was my opportunity to clear the air, but I had to think carefully about what I was going to say. I had to reel in the passion, since getting defensive and upset had got me nowhere last night. So I said with as much calmness as possible, 'Babe, I don't know if you've noticed, but I'm not in a very good place right now.' For the first time in ages, I felt like she was honestly listening and receptive. 'To say I'm having a crisis of faith would be an understatement, really. Like, you know actors? I'm like one of them on stage going, "What's my motivation," and instinctively I've always known what my next move is and what I do to get there. But I don't really know what that motivation is any more.'

'What was it before?' she asked.

'I know you'd all say men, but that's not it. They're just a by-product of having a laugh. But since Ben, I think I'm more aware of what people think of me now.

I'm not being funny, but I genuinely feel a major part of me has been crushed, and it's harder to get over. It's like we were all in this playground together getting messed around and messing others around. But now I'm playing solo, it's stopped being fun. And to see you with someone that once made me happy, that's not easy, hun. It's just a harsh reminder of what a tool I am. I mean, I've split up with a hundred per cent of the blokes I've ever gone out with. Those are just the worst stats ever. It's about time I got serious with someone. I know I can do it so long as someone better doesn't come along.'

'But you don't fancy Charlie, do you?' she asked.

'Nah, not at all. I suppose it's like another dent to my ego, though. A lot of people don't think I feel anything and I just roll with the punches. I totally don't, I feel every single one of them. I just don't voice it. Otherwise BHQ has won, right?'

'Bloody BHQ, they'll never beat us, hun. Can I just say something and tell you how it is from my perspective?' she said. I was seriously dreading anything she had to say. 'To be honest, I never saw you and Charlie together and proper loved-up. I only moved to the area in the last few months you were together and you didn't bring him out with you that often. It's like you were in denial. I get you've known each other since you were seventeen, but I've got no concept of that. Don't get me wrong, hun, I know I owe you. When you saved me from a life in Billericay you were like that bloke in *Pretty Woman*.'

'Hun, I'm no Edward Lewis and you're no prossie.'

'No, but you get what I'm saying? You just opened my world up and we totally went for it one hundred per cent. If you'd just get less touchy, we can carry on having a laugh like we always have.'

'I want that more than anything, but if you could understand that I'm a bit more fragile than I used to be then I think we'd avoid a whole lot more grief. Honestly, babe, you cannot talk to me about shagging Charlie yet. I'm sorry, hun, but I can't be that person for you if you're in that relationship. Not yet anyway.'

'Babe, I totally get you, and I know I don't think before I speak and usually you find that hilarious, but I totally get things have changed. I think you need to give me a codeword if I'm saying or doing anything that offends you.'

'Makes sense. How about Minge?' I said, and we both cracked up.

'So perfect, babe! How can I talk any more shite with that ringing in my ears. But can I just say this one thing before we start the Minge thing? You might be finding this whole thing weird, but I'm going through the motions too. If it's any consolation, I'm completely para that he still fancies you and I say as much all the time. He's totally getting sick of it. He denies it, but I never believe him.'

Strangely enough, that was a major consolation. It's funny – you see a couple and they seem all tight, but the only people who really know the truth are those two people in the relationship. The rest of us are just spectators. People can look all loved-up but they still got their hang-ups.

Is it wrong to feel reassured by your best mate's insecurities?

When the taxi finally rocked up (the same taxi driver, I might add. Either he's the only one in Marbs or we're good tippers. Or maybe he gets off on hysterical girls), Brooke gave me a massive hug and went, 'No more going in circles, yeah? This is it – honesty from now on or we might not make it through the next fall-out. I'm serious.'

'A hundred per cent, hun. I'll be yelling Minge left, right and centre just to shut you up. I mean, it's not like we've let a man get between us before.'

'And we're going to get your WEG crown back. No way am I letting some racing driver dicksplash get the better of you,' she said. 'You don't have to put on such a proud face in front of us lot, you know.'

'OK, I promise to wear my heart on my sleeve and break down at every given moment. Talking of dick-splashes, what did you make of that Brad?'

'Didn't like the bloke at all. I overheard him talking to one of his mates about Clio like she was a new car! Shit like, "yeah, I like a younger model. They've got more horsepower and a shiny chassis. Not many miles on the clock." Can you believe that?'

'Oh man, I feel bad because I pushed them together.'

'Don't feel bad. It's good for her to get involved. We all know she sticks to the sidelines, but I'm totally with you. She needs to get out there and play around. It's a numbers game at the end of the day, isn't it? The more blokes you meet, the higher the odds of you meeting the right one. It's just that he's not the winning ticket. By the way, I'm sorry I dragged you from that silver fox.'

'He wasn't exactly a grey-headed grandpa, hun. Though he would have been good for one thing and I'm not talking Scrabble.' It felt so good to be shooting the shit with Brooke again.

When we opened the door to the apartment, we found Cleo had only just sneaked in herself.

'I see, I see, the walk of shame, is it?' I said, teasing her. She went bright red. I'm so cruel to Cleo sometimes, but she loves it really.

'Maybe. A lady doesn't tell,' she replied.

'No, but you can. So what happened?' I demanded, but she just smirked and slipped off to bed. She is such a dark horse, that one. I think we can safely conclude she banged Brad. She seemed pretty happy about it so that's all that matters.

We got about three hours' sleep before I started getting hot and antsy. Our flights were later that evening and there was no way I was wasting any more time in my bed when I could be sunbathing. If you're properly hanging in PB, I highly recommend the roof terrace at Pangea. They play chillout tunes and it's not too busy and they bring food to you as you go in and out of consciousness. To be honest, that gas and air had sorted me right out so me and Brooke were raring to go. But guess which dirty stop-outs got back to the apartment at noon? Only Linda, Karen and Paula. They looked and smelt as good as three sweaty doner kebabs. Turns out they'd met some ravers who took them to this underground club, and because it was so dark, it didn't even occur to them it was late morning. But I had to give them respect because they were the last ones back. As predicted, Linda wanted to flip out when I told her about Gemma, but she was too weak so I just gave her the address of the hospital. I've never seen the woman look so broken. I said sleep it off for a couple of hours then go down the hospital. I gave her a Red Bull and told her to drink it when she woke up. Poor love, she probably hadn't pulled an all-nighter since 1983.

So it was just me, Cleo, Brooke, Emily and Ryan living the life on Pangea's rooftop sipping cocktails. Best cure after a heavy night is to get back on it.

I know a lot of people say they're sun worshippers, but they know nothing. I've spent years developing techniques to achieve the optimum tan. Always three hours on my front, three hours on my back, and the sun has to be behind me so it catches my shoulders, boobs and feet. And if I'm sunbathing for several days, I'll alternate the side I start on, reason being the first part of the day is the hottest, so that's optimum tanning time. I don't like to indulge one side more. And you're not going to get a deep tan if you're twisting and turning every few minutes. Imagine if you cooked a chicken like that? It'd take ages. You need to give one side a full-on three-hour blast.

I understand a lot of people don't have my kind of commitment when it comes to sunbathing, but more fool them. I won't go over my suntan lotion issues again, but just so you know, I use factor 30 everywhere if I'm in Spain. You cannot be mucking around with the sun there, and honestly, my tan is always the deepest. Just saying. The trick is in the slow, steady bake. Back in Essex, I obviously take it down to factor 15 since the sun's further away.

So it was three hours later that I was ready to turn on to my front. I always reapply my lotion during the turn, so I called Ryan over to do my back, but he was already on his way. He chucked this magazine down on the sunlounger and looked at me expectantly.

'*Hola!* magazine, babe? I'm having enough trouble just speaking English today.'

'Look at it, yeah? Does anyone look familiar in these party pictures?' he asked.

I gave it a quick scan and there was my Spanish actor buddying up to Javier Bardem.

'Oh my days, I don't believe it. I was one degree from Javier!' I'll confess, I've got quite an unhealthy obsession with him. To the point that I feel rage when I see Penélope Cruz. He's a total beast of a man and there's not many of them left.

'You got his number though, yeah?'

'I thought I did,' I said and started scrolling down my contacts. I had no idea what I'd saved it under. Helpfully, I hadn't put it under his name – that would have been too easy. As I was searching, I heard the word 'bubbla' float across the rooftop. My new best friend! And Brad was with her too. Interesting. I would be watching Cleo's body language like a hawk.

'Doll, pop yourself next to me. This is prime tanning time,' I said excitedly.

'I so don't want to go home tomorrow. What fun's Essex in August? It's cold, miserable and grey,' she lamented. 'Why do we put up with it, bubs? Why can't we just live out here?'

'Well, we could if we wanted,' I said. 'Like, I could open an amazing swimwear store. What do you do anyway?'

'Not much, just go around, go out, cause a stir,' she said.

'Ummm, I'm not being funny, but that's more of a calling than a trade. Like, what could you sell?'

'I am a trained beautician. It's just that I haven't worked for a year.'

'You're still a beautician, though. People are crying out for lash extensions and spray-tans out here. Have you seen the business Golden Tarts get? You could steal their clients easily, hun.'

'That sounds a bit cut-throat, bubbla.'

'No, it's just healthy competition. I can mentor you if you want?'

'Nah, it's alright. Me dad sorts me out so I'm fine for now,' she said.

Gotta say, I felt a bit disappointed in my new best friend's lack of sparkiness. Turned out her dad was a minted barrister's clerk, which is exactly what my rich brother-in-law Tony does. This career path is a proper Essex-boy phenomenon. You'll see them getting off at Liverpool Street station in droves, these wide boys, suited and booted and heading to their various chambers. Basically, they're the wheeler-dealers of the legal world, getting in the cases, negotiating the fees, then taking their cut of it. And I'm talking serious money, like six-figure salaries, and most have worked their way up from the age of sixteen. You just need the gift of the gab and a steady nerve, but that's your typical Essex man in a nutshell. I wasn't surprised Lauren had no motivation to work because some minted girls are like that. But if I'm to be honest, I felt a bit sorry for her. I can't judge, though, just because I like a faster pace of life. Perhaps I needed to make Lauren my new project when I got home?

I looked over to see Cleo and Brad flirting, so clearly that had gone very well. You know what I say – one woman's dicksplash is another woman's soulmate. But you'll never guess what I saw? Scratches all down Brad's back. Obviously the only way is rough sex for Cleo. It's always the quiet ones.

After we'd milked the sun for every last drop of its harmful rays, we had to accept the holiday was over. We had left plenty of time to pack, and were expecting Linda to be back with an update on Gemma. Except when we got back to the apartment, she hadn't even moved from her stinking bed since we'd left her. Unbelievable. This caused a massive row with a lot of finger pointing on all sides. Honestly, we'd never have gone sunbathing if we'd known she'd been abandoned by her own mother. Gemma hadn't even tried calling any of us, probably because she was sobbing her little heart out in a Spanish ward.

Just as our shouting subsided, all our phones went off at the same time. I thought, shit, Gem's sent a group text disowning us, but it was from our good mates at easyJet telling us they'd cancelled our flight. Yeah, the one that was due to take off in three hours' time. We had shunned the expensive return flights on Ryanair for the cheaper easyJet option. So when Ryanair mugged us off, we were all smug that they weren't getting our custom on the way back. Not to be superstitious here, but you should never congratulate yourself until you're home and dry. I am so sure Ryanair and easyJet are business partners with BHQ and whenever they sense smugness, they take you down. No one is untouchable, not even easyJet employees. So our options were, get your money back and book another flight, or wait three days for the next available flight out. Cleo was completely breaking down, saying she needed to get back for work, which wasn't very helpful since we were all in the same boat. We called Gem (who was too sedated to even be mad at us) and found out they needed to put a metal plate in her wrist and they'd be operating on her the next day. That sealed the deal. Me and Brooke would selflessly wait it out in Puerto Banus by Gemma's side for the next three days and the rest of them would get a flight out in the morning. That gave us enough time to visit Gemma that evening with a very guilty Linda in tow.

I won't lie to you, me and Brooke had a delightful time once we'd shifted all those hens. We'd pop to the hospital for a couple of hours, lie by a beach-club pool for a couple more, back to the hospital, then we'd finish the night with a lovely meal for two in the marina. Considering all the bad shit that had gone down, I'd say our friendship had become ten times stronger. I highly recommend taking a few days' holiday after a hen do, though ideally not with the bride-to-be lying in a hospital bed.

Flattery Gets You Everywhere

The wedding was in the first week of September, so by the time we got back to Essex it was only four weeks until the big day. Gem was on a lot of drugs, which seemed to send her a bit loopy-loo. One minute she'd be all dazed and the next she was all irate. Understandably, she was pretty upset that all her wedding pictures would now feature a white cast. At least it matched her dress, though, right?

Normally, I love the fact that Gem's a proud, strong, independent woman, but that was a major issue now she was coping with a new disability. She totally did my nut in. Just by chance, we dropped over one evening and she opened the door looking like old man Benjamin Button. Turned out Grant had gone straight to football after work while she'd been in the house starving the whole day. We got a takeaway in and had such a go at Grant the moment he got in, but he said Gem had told him to go to football. We had to explain to him that you can't take what girls say at face value. He didn't get it. I ask you, how long had he been with Gem and he still didn't know the basics?

We had to get tough with Gemma if she was going to get at all better. When she said she was fine, help was forced on her and protests ignored. Shopping, driving, beautifying, you name it, we did it. She couldn't even open a champagne bottle. The sooner this hell was over, the better. The one thing we couldn't help her with was her work. Obviously her hands are her tools so she had to cancel a load of jobs at first. But as she got more confident with the cast, she began to work the one-handed make-up artist thing. You cannot keep a WEG down for long. We're too resourceful. And I won't lie, there were perks for us too. People flocked to us when we were out because they're nosy and had to know how she'd done it. We got served quickly at bars and jumped every taxi queue. The downside was a lot of people made the same jokes to her like, 'Doesn't look like you'll be playing the piano again,' or even worse, 'At least you got one working hand,' and then winked at her. Also, drunk people kept trying to sign her pristine white cast which would make her flip out. Who knew so many people carried Sharpies around?

There was one epic night in late August which turned out to be our last big blow-out before the wedding. Jake was celebrating his twenty-fourth and had chosen Funky Mojoe as his venue. Now, this bit has already started off bad because I've already expressed my hatred for this place and it's also the location that Grant pulled his bunny-boiler (not that Gem knows that). So I wasn't really looking forward to going out that evening, but in these situations, you've got to completely own the night yourself. And Brooke had already done that for us. Hilariously, she had gone for an audition for *TOWIE* earlier that day. It still cracks me up thinking about it. She'd been majorly gutted when she found out she'd missed the auditions down Nu Bar, but a few days later opportunity came knocking and someone on her late-night Friday flight said they were going to the *TOWIE* auditions at Faces the next day.

Me and Brooke always find this happens to us. Like, we'll want something so badly and it just seems to come to us without even trying. I suppose we're abnormally lucky, so maybe BHQ works on two levels, the giving and the taking. So yeah, they might have shoved glass in Brooke's foot and created our fallout, but hadn't they now served up a second chance at the auditions? Although when shit like that happens, I think, what are BHQ up to? You can never get too comfortable, believe me.

When you audition, they tell you you must either 'live in, work in or come from Essex'. Brooke came into the shop that morning and ran through her audition speech with us. She wanted to storm in there going I'm born, bred, live and work in Essex just so they knew she was one hundred per cent WEG. But I pointed out that even though she flew to and from Stansted every day, technically she worked in the sky. Just saying. Brooke was having none of it and walked out, slamming the shop door behind her. Charming! I can't help it if I'm the voice of truth.

Didn't matter what I said, though, because I knew she'd kill it in those auditions. I mean, we were under no illusion that she'd become a main cast member, but they'd have to put someone like her in a few scenes. They'd be blind not to. She later admitted that when they asked about any dramas going on in her life, she told them about us two and Charlie. I mean, what if the producers called us all up to appear in the show and re-enact all our clashes? How embarrassing. I'm sorry, but I so wasn't up for being exploited just so I could get my face on TV. I'm famous enough in West Essex as it is.

Once I'd knocked off work, I sped back home to get ready for our South Woodford night, but I was desperate to see Marilyn's wedding outfit so I made a pit stop at Puppy Kit. As soon as I'd heard about this woman from Dior who designed couture doggy hats, I'd given the dog boutique my vision, and they'd totally delivered. Oh my days, he looked so fly! Picture this: a white top hat covered in Swarovski crystals with a white feather on the side, teamed up with a snazzy little white tux jacket.

Essentially, he was the dog version of Fred Astaire. Marilyn would be pulling *all* the bitches in that get-up.

His cuteness totally distracted me from my own wardrobe agenda, so I had to give Gem a bell for inspiration. She reminded me that I hadn't worn my fitted red French Connection dress, which would go perfectly with my red bio-gels. So obvious! Why hadn't I thought of it? Throw into the mix my favourite black-and-white leopard print Miu Miu heels and my patent red Chloé clutch, and job done. Thanks to the glorious Puerto Banus sun, I hadn't needed a spray since being back, but while I was getting my nails done in Belles I held my arm up to the beautician's and I was forced to admit I was fading. Lauren had been right – it was grey and miserable here in August. But to be fair, Belles browned me up a treat.

My cab was running later than me for once, so I had time to stick my head into the house and find out what Jake's plans were. I could not believe my eyes. He was stood there in these tight jeans, a V-neck black t-shirt and these ridiculous sheepskin slipper boots. I told him he looked like he'd robbed a granny, and he replied, 'But they're Paul Smith, everyone's wearing Zowies.' Honestly, I despair sometimes. I've tried telling him that women always judge a bloke by his shoes, but he just doesn't listen.

'If you don't want to get chucked out of your own party, you seriously need to reassess your footwear, love,' I said. I mean, what was Paul Smith on?

We weren't going to go straight to Mojoe's as it would be tragically early, but the plan was to warm up in a bar down George Lane. Brooke was harping on about Lizard Lounge, but me and Gem were in the mood for Switch Bar. It's one of the bars they always film the *TOWIE* lot in having heart-to-hearts over a coffee. Like that's how we spend our afternoons in West Essex. All heart-to-hearts happen when we're lashed-up – we don't make special appointments for them. We're just like the rest of you, you know.

In the end me and Gem won, not that Brooke was that cut-up since she'd come straight from her audition and was on a massive high. She looked stunning considering she'd only had twenty-four hours to prepare. I kid you not, she was wearing this strapless leather dress which had a bodice built into it. Only she had the confidence to pull off a number like that. It was one hundred per cent dominatrix. She was giving us the low-down on the audition when she was hit by a memory jolt.

'Oh my God, guess who I saw there?'

'I can't guess. There's a lot of people to go through. Cheryl and Sue?'

'Incorrect. I saw the delightful Vicki P.'

'Bloody Bucket! How would she ever get a part, anyway? It requires hanging out with girls,' I said.

'You should have seen her walking down the queue before her audition. She gave a death stare to any girl that was pretty and gave the eye to any fit blokes. And she actually came up to me and went, "That's an interesting dress. Is that from Ann Summers?" so I just went, "Nah, it's Givenchy, actually. Same one Victoria Beckham has," and she did one of her smirks. She knew I was bullshitting. And I happened to be eating a McFlurry at the time and she goes, "You do know you might as well be eating a tub of fat," and I just replied, "I'm really lucky, I never put on weight, so things like that never occur to me."'

'What a prize bitch. She was completely trying to psych you out,' I said. 'So funny – she never comes over to us when we're together, but when we're separated from the herd, she pounces.'

'Screw her. Everyone else does,' Gem suddenly piped up. She was clearly ending our bitchfest, but didn't seem very talkative that night.

'What's going on with you, hun?'

'I had some shitty news yesterday,' said Gem. 'The surgeon at Holly House has looked at my latest wrist X-ray and they want to operate again.'

'Oh hun, that's so awful. Did they leave something in your wrist? I've seen programmes about that.'

'They said the plate had shifted so they'll have to break it again and insert sturdy pins instead. And they're doing it on Tuesday.'

'Fuck, that's cutting it a bit fine, isn't it, Gem?' I said. 'That's, what . . . four days before the wedding. What if they botch it up?'

'It was either that or I get it done after the wedding, which would mean cancelling the honeymoon. I'm not missing out on that,' she said. 'Apparently, on a scale of one to eight, this break is an eight,' she added.

'I can't believe this. We never should have let you dance on that sofa,' said Brooke.

'Don't blame yourselves. If it makes you feel any better, it's done wonders for my love life. I've had to be completely reliant on Grant, like, he's had to wash my hair every morning, cook all the meals, do up my bra . . .'

'That'll be a first for Grant,' Brooke said.

'Shut up! I'm serious. Getting engaged is all well and good, but it's taken this to make us proper close. I've properly fallen in love with him all over again and we're at it all the time. Like when he first saw me all casted up, he was properly cut-up. You know Grant doesn't do crying. But he was really going for it and went, "I don't believe it, the two things I love the most, broken." So I said, "What you talking about?" and he goes, "First my iPhone and now you," and he just cried like a baby.'

'Awww, that's proper moving, hun. I'm so glad you guys have finally got there,' gushed Brooke.

'Oh my God, I haven't even told you the best bit of all this,' she said. Me and Brooke were all ears. 'You know he was all shady about what he got up to with the boys before? Now he's gone the other way and feels the need to confess everything to me.'

'Oh my God, amazing! What sort of stuff has he blabbed about?' Brooke asked.

'Well, he's only told me this because he's scared Charlie's going to mention it in the best man speech, but a lot of bad stuff happened on the stag. Like they hired a boat in Amsterdam to do a river cruise, but they picked up two strippers on the way. He said it was awful because they kept going under all these bridges and families would be looking over and see this full-on sex show go past. These girls were butt-naked, and as far as I can make out he was just topless but forced to lick whipped cream off their tats. I can't even be mad at that because he was tied up at the time.'

'It's good to know the man I'm dating organized this entertainment,' said Brooke sarcastically. 'It restores my faith in men.'

'Believe it or not, it does get worse, babe. They then dress him up in a tight lycra dress that shows every bulge and force him to wear heels and a black wig. So the first bar they go to that night, there's nobody there but this dwarf. So Grant gets talking to him and suddenly the boys whip out a pair of handcuffs and chain Grant to the dwarf. They've only gone and hired the little guy for the night!'

'That seems like a really shit job for the dwarf,' I said.

'Nah, wait for it, because there's a happy ending for him. So anyway, everyone gets more and more off their face. Grant's struggling to walk much further in heels by this point. Then one of the stags, I'm not saying it was Charlie, goes, "We've bought you an hour with a prostitute."'

'Urghh, gross,' I said. Sorry, but blokes are so wrong sometimes.

'Let me finish. So they're all cheering for him as he follows this prossie through a doorway, and obviously the dwarf is still handcuffed to him. So when they're in the room and she's taking off her clothes, Grant goes, "Listen, I'm sorry, I don't want to do this. I really love my girlfriend and I can't do this to her." How sweet is that? So then the dwarf pipes up, "Well, since she's paid for and you're not going to do her, do you mind if I do?" Well what could Grant say? So he had to sit against the bed as the dwarf went for it.'

Brooke and Gemma were cackling away, but it was all a bit too *Twin Peaks* for my liking. I didn't get how Gemma was reading this as the most romantic gesture ever when basically Grant had been with two strippers, a dwarf and a prostitute all in one day. And that's just the bits Grant told her about!

As revealing a gossip fest as this was, we had to drink up and get ourselves to Mojoe's. Even though it was only eight hundred metres away, we still got a cab. You might think that's mental, but this is where so many London women get it wrong. The number of times I've seen a woman balancing in a piss-soaked doorway as she takes off her flat shoes, puts on heels and then totters into a bar like nothing ever happened. And it means they've got to carry around a massive bag for their shoes all night, which is just embarrassing. Do you think that's how Elizabeth Taylor did it back in the day? Have some dignity. Nah, the trick is to leave the house in heels and then just cab it everywhere or you just suck it up. You've got to be true to yourself, and these part-timers are just lying to themselves that they're a hundred per cent glam. It honestly makes me so mad.

If you've watched *TOWIE*, you'll know Mojoe's because it featured pretty prominently in the third series. It's where Jess and her mum held their joint birthday (like that would ever happen), and where Mark and Arg clashed with Lucy, Mario and Lydia. When they film at Mojoe's, it gets people raging around here and it's all to do with postcodes. Let me explain: Funky Mojoe is in South Woodford, E18, a London postcode. So people say how can it star in *TOWIE*? But then one mile up the high road is Woodford Green which is IG8, an Essex postcode, and that's where Lydia and Arg live. Just to complicate things, both places are in the same London Borough.

In my opinion, the definition of West Essex goes beyond postcodes. Both places are very much West Essex in their vibe as far as nightlife goes, but neither is a patch on the Golden Triangle lifestyle. Neither of the Woodfords has enough clothes shops and beauty salons for starters. And Woodford's got more boozers than bars and South Woodford's George Lane is a bit ordinary if you ask me. So yeah, they give the West Essex thing a go but things are a bit more upmarket in Buckhurst Hill, Chigwell and Loughton. I mean, you just wouldn't get a place like Sheesh in South Woodford. I'm sorry if that upsets some people, but deal with it. Mojoe's is next door to an old people's home, so the facts really speak for themselves there.

Anyways, I told you about the shooting and stabbings that have happened there, right? People get glassed there too, and Danielle Lloyd got punched in the face once. But then this club keeps the punters coming by paying big bucks to celebs to make personal appearances. Apparently, Pamela Anderson was paid £12,000 just to show up, and people off *The X Factor* are always performing there, but the only time I was tempted was when Amy Winehouse played. She was good, even if she was out of it. A few idiots felt cheated because she only sang a couple of tunes, but it was never meant to be a gig, was it? No pleasing some people. Amy Winehouse's Aunt Lily ran a legendary chippy in South Woodford called Woods – true story that. But she sold it and retired just after Amy died. Proper sad, but the chips are still amazing.

As usual, Mojoe's was bumper-to-bumper with white limos out front. Jake had only got us on the guest list, so we had to queue. They didn't go for Gem waving her cast about. Out-bloody-rageous. So I kept going up to the doorman and badgering him. I was eventually forced to say that Gem had broken her wrist in Mojoe's, so the least they could do was let us in. Persistence and lies pay.

I saw Jake sat in front of a line of shots, downing them one after another. It was going to be one messy night, but I was relieved to see he had normal shoes on. I'd honestly been worrying for hours about that. Before I could even get to Jake's reserved area, his mate Jamie put his arm around my shoulder. Bit keen. I can't even remember what we were talking about because I can't listen to people if I haven't settled in somewhere with a drink. It's like I haven't properly entered the venue. But I do remember thinking, he's made a proper effort with his look again. Tight black shirt, brown belt, dark blue trousers and brown shoes. He was looking so fine but it still felt a bit weird with him being Jake's mate. Also, I was sober enough to remember how rude I was to him in Monaco. What can I say, he caught me at a highly emotional time and I was due on. I saw Brooke waving me over at the bar so I made my excuses.

Is there a barman in Essex Brooke *hasn't* done, I ask you? Thanks to her, it was free rosé all round. Although I don't think Brooke's former fling was a member of Mensa because I heard her go, 'Awww, you're so sweet, we'll have three glasses of wine, please.' He asks, 'Large or small?' Brooke goes, 'Aren't you meant to ask me which wine I want?' He just shrugs his shoulder and says, 'I don't know, do I?' It was no Mayfair Hotel.

The first glass went down very nicely, and just as I was about to get another round in, I saw someone striding towards the bar but looking right at me. When Ben reached me I thought, I'm in for it now. Keep in mind this was the first time I'd seen him since I'd done damage to his car.

'Alright?' he goes.

'Yeah, you?'

'Not bad. Just got myself a Porsche, so all's good in the world. Someone trashed my last car.' He seemed weirdly happy, which was unnerving. Where was the slanging match?

'Listen, can I talk to you?' he continued.

'Yeah, if you want, but you can do it right here. I'm not moving from the bar. What you doing here anyway? You hate this place as much as me.'

'Saw on Facebook that you were here tonight, didn't I?' Epic error. I'm going to get myself killed one day if all my stalkers keep looking on that. 'Babe, just hear me out. I haven't been able to stop thinking about you after everything that happened last month. I actually respect what you did. I totally deserved it. Until you came along, I was bored and just fucked birds for a laugh. But when we were together, we had a good time, didn't we? And I think I treated you nice apart from that last bit. I was a fucking idiot and I get it was a horrible thing to do. But you and me are the same, Becs. We live life to the full, we're over the top, and life isn't boring with you around.'

'Well, I dunno,'

'And babe, I need to thank you. That American guy is paying for me to go out to California to try my hand at NASCAR. I got a pocketful of cash to celebrate and I want to spend it on you and your mates.'

'Oh, so he wasn't pissed that he got nothing in the trade-off? That's decent of him. Look, I just want you to stay away from me, please. We did have a good time, but that's over now.'

'So you don't want to hear what I've got to say? Becs, I've come here because I want you to come to America with me. I promise things will be a whole lot better, babe. We could kill it out there, just the two of us.'

'Meh.' I shrugged. 'I'm fine in Essex, thanks. This conversation's over, by the way,' I said and turned back to the bar.

I was actually all sorts of confused, but I wasn't going to let him know that. I couldn't figure out if the player had turned or was still playing me. Amazingly, that Gino loser wasn't out with him that night. Maybe he'd ditched him too? Maybe he led Ben astray the whole time? I mean, he was about fifteen years older so he probably had some sort of hold over him. I just had to push it to the back of my mind. There's a reason people break up and ours was better than most.

Since no one else was offering to buy, I got us another bottle of Mojoe's finest rosé and brought it over to Jake's table. I completely blocked out Ben even when the girls tried to discuss it with me. How silly – I was actually having to fight the urge to be with him after all he'd done. But you know what, he couldn't click his fingers and I'd go back to him. Who'd he think he was, Mark Wright? And that would have made me Lauren or Lucy or whoever else. No thank you, not my style.

It wasn't hard to distract myself. There were so many fit blokes in the room I could hardly see straight. Who knew Mojoe's contained such hidden talent? Could have been the rosé glasses, though. There were a couple of groups who definitely had potential. You know all those fleeting glances women give blokes in Jane Austen films? That technique doesn't work in Mojoe's. Catch their eye by all means, but you got to follow that up. So this is how you work it. Debrief the girls on the blokes you're approaching. When everyone knows the target, you'll work better as a team. Then place yourselves within talking distance of the blokes. If they're still not biting, it's up to you. I personally always like to flatter them on their choice of shirt. It's boring but effective. Once you're talking, you're flying. Now imagine you hadn't done all this and had just carried on glancing at him across the room? Taxi for one.

I don't think society has realized that it's women who have to make all the moves these days. People like

Cleo are still in denial, but the reality is, men don't approach women. Hang on, let me rephrase that. The quality men don't approach women. The complete tools have no problem. They've been dealt so many knock-backs that they've become immune to failure. I mean, Ben came up to me when we first met, didn't he? And it was via Gino, just to make it ten times worse.

In the end, we got talking to a couple of semi-pros (one was a semi-pro actor, which was new to me. He'd even had his face put on his business cards). We all made our excuses, and ended up spending most of the night with a bunch of lads from Leytonstone. They weren't flash or anything, just good fun boys and proper fit too. There's a really good test to see how classy a bloke is. You just ask them for a mojito. If they ask what that is, then you're going to go on some really shit dates. Needless to say, these boys were clueless so they wouldn't be getting my real number, but I did end up snogging one of them. I just thought, what's the harm? Hopefully it would get the message through to Ben too. We didn't stick with them all night, though. You should always walk away from blokes, whether you're interested or not. Like, I didn't want these boys to get too attached, so you got to know when to do the cut-off. But if you do like the bloke, you still walk away because you got to leave them wanting more – but keep looking over. Anyways, these boys wanted us to go on to O'Neill's in Leyton-stone, so that was another strike against them. If you've ever been stuck to the floor there, you'll know exactly why I wasn't tempted. When we went back over to Jake's table, I saw Jamie was chatting to some blonde dollybird. Clearly, I'd missed that boat. Bit of a shame as I thought there'd been a flicker between us earlier. But I suppose I'd done a bit of a Cleo and acted uninterested. See what happens if you don't turn on the charm offensive?

Just as I was waving a fist at BHQ, the most amazing thing happened. I just wish I'd taken a picture but I was too stunned to think of it at the time. This girl comes out the toilets and I swear to you, she's dripping in sick. Oh my days, it was horrific, and it was all over her hair. Then I saw Ben walk out straight behind her and he had a proper sick beard going on. I think we can all guess what happened here. The only thing that could have made this any better was if it had been Bucket.

We needed more details, so Brooke sidled up to the girl, who was now sobbing uncontrollably. She didn't get too close in case she got puke on her leathers, but this poor, naïve girl had basically followed Ben into the toilets, given him a blowie and he'd hurled right on top of her. It gave a whole new meaning to blowing your load.

My gut reaction was, 'Oh my God, that could have been me.' Brooke advised her to go back into the toilets and sort herself. When she reemerged with slightly fewer chunks in her extensions, I shoved a glass of champagne into her hand. 'I just wanted you to have this. I thought it might take the edge off things,' I said, and she looked at me all confused. So I just smiled at her and walked back to the others. If it had been me, that's what I'd want someone to do. I considered the gesture a bit of a karma thing. I thought, yeah, watch and weep, BHQ. Of course I'd got me and the girls a glass too and we toasted my lucky escape. The spell had well and truly been broken.

I didn't want to be in the club when the lights went up. That's my worst thing ever because you're all in this amazing club bubble, but when the lights come on, reality seems a lot bleaker than usual. By this point Jake was doing some sort of Russian dancing, so I found Jamie to help me get him out and into a taxi. Except Jake wasn't going easily and insisted on going to Kebab-land first. He bloody loves that place. While I waited outside with Jamie, he goes to me, 'I don't know what you ever saw in that prick anyway. I thought the Essex elite had better taste than that.'

'Yeah, yeah, all very well for people to tell me that now. Anyways, you saw how good it was in Monaco and it was like that all the time with Ben. One big Monaco.'

'I didn't think it was that great,' he replied.

'What do you mean? You were living the high life with Taio Cruz, sipping on gin and juice, partying till dawn. I bet you even got to see the bloody Grand Prix.'

'What you talking about? I wasn't partying with Taio Cruz.'

'That's what Jake said. Did he get confused with Tom Cruise or something? He's a bit dyslexic like that.'

'He said that? That's weird. I mean, I work at a studio he's been to before, but I don't really know the fella. I was only at that flash party because I gatecrashed.'

'Sorry, what?'

'Me and my mates were staying in Nice and we thought there'd be a bit of a buzz going on in Monaco, found the hotel, sneaked in and yeah, technically we did party with Taio Cruz if you mean we were in the same building.'

'So you just blagged your way in . . . in *those* clothes?'

'That's about the long and short of it. Then after I left you, I followed signs to the beach and slept there.'

'Oh my God, that's proper impressive, hun,' I said. Why hadn't I thought of that instead of running away and catching the first plane out? You live and learn, right?

Jake finally emerged with his shish, but we had to make him act sober so a taxi would take us. After we'd shoved Jake in the back seat, I was just getting in myself when Jamie grabs my hand and goes, 'You know, Becs, I got a lot of time for you.'

We stood there for a moment and I wanted to say something so genuine back to him, but as usual, I killed the moment and went, 'Oh, great, another stalker. That's all I need, hun.'

He smiled and I let go of his hand. Just then Jake

stuck his head out the window and shouted, 'Look, Ben's still here!' and I looked over and there he was slumped up against the old people's home. I decided I had to seize the moment, so I grabbed Jamie's face and kissed him right on the lips. He looked shocked, possibly a bit scared, so I quickly jumped in the taxi to make my getaway.

As we drew away, Jake stuck his head back out the window and shouted, 'Stay lucky, son,' as he aimed his kebab at Ben's head. Obviously he missed, but it's the thought that counts.

17

Essex Up Those in Need

Four days before the wedding of the year, BHQ unleashed one of their cruellest jokes yet. I went to the hospital the afternoon after Gem had her second wrist operation. Holly House is a private hospital, so it was a step up from the Spanish one. She had a room all to herself and her arm was strapped up high in a foam support. When I went in, she had a face like thunder.

'Hun, how you feeling?'

'Shit. Just have a look for yourself,' she said. I bent my head round to get a proper look and I could not believe it. They'd turned her into Edward Scissorhands. Where she'd had a neat white cast there was now a monstrosity of an arm with some sort of construction built on top.

'What have they done to you?' I said, horrified.

'As agreed, they pinned my wrist. But nobody bloody mentioned the pins would be on the *outside*. It's like they've built a load of scaffolding on my arm and wrapped it in loads of bandages. I look like a fucking freak.'

'Has the surgeon been round yet?'

'Nah, course not. He'll be out playing golf, but I'm going to get so mad when he does show his face. I mean, how am I meant to do anything with this on, let alone get married. I can't believe this is happening.'

I couldn't deny it, she did look like a freak. What a thing to do to someone. I told her not to worry about a thing, me and Brooke would be her wedding co-ordinators. I also promised to put posh Emily up at mine when she came for the wedding. Problem was, we hadn't exactly clicked at the hen do because I'd felt her eyes on me the whole time. I'm aware that makes me sound para, but that's how it felt. I didn't know if I'd be comfortable with her in my cottage in case she watched me in my sleep, but I had to do it for Gem.

The reception was at Gem's mum and step-dad's in Stapleford Abbotts. They'd hired this incredible marquee which came complete with chandeliers. Their place is in the middle of nowhere (or East Bumblefuck, as Brooke calls it), so it was a right pain to get to, but most of the jobs left to do were just follow-up calls, so we didn't have to make too many trips. We had it so under control. I personally delivered Gem's dress to her the day she got out of hospital as I thought it would cheer her up, but when she saw her bionic arm against the Vera Wang, she had a major hissy. Even when I tried wrapping her arm in some silk fabric, it just looked like we'd hidden a massive lobster claw. She was not only finding the weight of the thing an issue, but she was in way more pain than before. I felt completely helpless. At the end of the day, her big day had been pissed on.

As much as I was trying to stay focused, I had also started texting Jamie. Nothing saucy, just meaningless banter. I really didn't want to commit myself to anything as he wasn't someone I could just muck around with for a couple of months if he was mates with Jake. Not to blow my own trumpet, he was also scarily into me and that's not to be played with. I know I've said the same about Charlie already, but a girl just knows. When a bloke starts calling me 'Miss Fox' that's a clear sign they want a piece. I can't tell you the psychology behind it, it's just a fact. And I found out what all that Taio Cruz business was about. Jake had basically fed me 'white lies' because he thought that would get me interested in Jamie. Does he honestly think I'm that shallow? I've fallen for lots of men who don't mix with the rich and famous.

Marilyn and I reluctantly picked up posh Emily from Buckhurst Hill station on the Friday. She wanted to have a quick look around which was a bit annoying as I had stuff to do, but we took her up Queens Road for a caffeine hit at the Queen's Tea Rooms. Her eyes were coming out her head as we walked up, and then she turns to me and goes, 'I can't believe this place.' I suppose it must have been a bit of a culture shock.

We sat in the window of the café and Emily just wouldn't stop with the questions. Like, every time a nice car went down the road she asked me what make it was because apparently I'm some sort of expert. Or if a woman walked past she asked me what work she'd had done. I thought it was a bit racist of her to assume that all WEGs have been worked on. And she couldn't get her head round people going in and out of the shops on a Friday afternoon. Didn't they have jobs? she asked. I dunno, do I, but I reckon the women work a lot harder than the blokes round here, so let them have Friday afternoon off. I decided Emily was one of those girls who can't think outside the box. Then she goes to me, 'I would love to be that glam-looking all the time. Must take so much time and effort, though.'

'It's not for part-timers, but you can't put a price on confidence, hun. I mean, we could always get you a little something – you know, treat yourself before the wedding?'

'Well, I did look a bit pale and sickly in all the pictures from the hen do,' she replies. It was music to my ears.

'Please, Em, let me do a good thing. Let me Essex you up,' I said, all excited.

'I don't know. I was only thinking I could do with a bit of colour,' she replied.

'Promise we won't go over the top, just let me show you what's out there,' I said. She was still looking unsure, so I carried on, 'If you were a bridesmaid at an Asian wedding, you'd get all involved in the dress and rituals right? A bit of henna here, a bindi there? Same difference, babe. It's important to respect our ways, and I promise you, you'll feel one hundred per cent better as a result. We got a saying round here: You gotta fake it to make it. Do you or do you not want to make it in life?'

After that rousing little speech, how could she say no? I wasn't being horrible, I just really wanted to help her out.

Considering I'd been dreading hanging out with Emily, it turned out to be the most exhilarating few hours I've had in a long time. Belles worked on her nails, but I drove her to Loughton for the rest because I had a surprise in store. First off, I took her to my special woman who does eyelash extensions for dirt cheap. Sorry, I can't give away her identity because, as per usual, it's all cash in hand, wink, wink, nudge, nudge. She did such a stunning job, and even though Emily was all scared I'd give her full-on Bambi lashes, she was jumping for joy when she saw the results. Got myself done while I was there too.

Then I took her to Fakin' It for a spray. She only agreed to a Light FakeBake, but what you going to do? I'd shown her how my two-day-old dark tan was fading already, but she was having none of it. In retrospect it was for the best, because I forgot that not everyone exfoliates, so she would have had serious streaking. Though she did let them sort out her eyebrows while we were there, thank God.

Then the icing on the cake: I took her for a cut and blow-dry with David Beckham's sister at HOB. She couldn't believe it, but I told Emily to keep her cool and not ask Jo any questions about David. Like if Jake were famous, I wouldn't want people banging on about him in my shop. I'm my own person, I'm there to find wedding dresses, end of. Jo's a serious party girl and a Loughton local, so I always see her down Nu Bar and the likes. I honestly can't imagine her and Victoria in the same room together, though. Like, Jo says it how she sees it, whereas old VB seems a bit uptight. Just saying. She says she's definitely going to open up her own salon one day, but if you ask me, she's too busy having fun.

Despite Emily's claims she'd had her highlights done recently she still needed a Brazilian blow-dry to get rid of that frizzball in my opinion. Why wouldn't you want three months of groomed perfection? No word of a lie, Emily's hair was a shorter version of Lydia Bright's mum's hairdo, but she said she was drawing the line. Can't win them all, I suppose. I saw her going through her receipts as I was getting my hair blow-dried, so I think the truth of it was I'd spent too much of her cash, even though I'd treated her to the eyelashes. I'd done what I could, and she was lucky she had nice teeth and a good rack already. She just needed the right bra is all, so I sorted her out at Pretty Things.

She's got a stunning figure, so as soon as we got back to mine, I stuck her in a few of my outfits. When she came out for the big reveal, the fruit of our labours was evident. I felt like I'd just given birth to my own WEG baby, except she spoke proper. As soon as she popped those heels on, you could see her get some attitude. I should start some sort of charity for people like her – you know, people who need their sexy back.

We drove over to Gem's mum's for an evening of pampering and champers for her last night of freedom. All the girls were totally blown away by what I'd achieved, and in turn Emily was glowing with the compliments. Just so long as her frizz didn't fight the blow-dry, we were golden.

*

I remember waking up the next day and lying there all woozy with sleep and just waiting for my brain to tell me why my body was surging with excitement. I love a wedding day morning! Although that woozy sleep thing can go the other way when you wake up with a sense of dread, thinking, Why do I feel so sad? Oh yeah, my boyfriend had a threesome without me. Not that I was dwelling on shit like that after seeing a text from Jamie wishing me good luck. It was pretty thoughtful, but you can't get suckered in just because people are being nice to you, so I gave a warm but distant thanks back.

I then woke up Emily, who was still looking fabulous half asleep. Mum had cooked us the works for breakfast, but when we were tidying up after ourselves, Mum goes, 'Aren't you a nice, polite girl, Emily? Becci never loads the dishwasher normally,' which just made her blush. Mum talks to all our friends like they're still twelve. And Dad just went about the house singing, 'I'm getting married in the morning, ding-dong the bells are going to chime.' I shoved Emily out before she saw any more.

We got to Gem's crazy early because five bridesmaids, one bride and one mother-of-the-bride is quite a lot of work for two hair-and-make-up girls. I went first and it was all going pretty well until we got to the hair. I hadn't had a blow-dry just for this girl to stick my hair to my head. I had to be tactful, though, because they were mates of Gem's. So I just went, 'Does it look big enough to you?' She got the message and brushed it out, backcombed, sprayed, put it back up, sprayed again. That's what I'm talking about. Thank God I went first or we'd all have been flatheads.

It was a pretty lush morning drinking Buck's Fizz and eating cake. And I had a little gift for Gem. I know she was hating all that material I'd wrapped around her arm before, but I'd thought long and hard about a solution and I'd come up with my own creation, the Bling

Sling. What I'd done was get this seriously crystallized veil that had been hanging round the stockroom for months, if not years, and sewed a section of it onto Gem's bionic arm so it was the perfect fit and super-light. Alright, so it wasn't a sling, but you get what I'm saying, I vajazzled her bandage. I honestly think there's a market for this, because how many other girls are wandering around out there feeling unglamorous just because they got broken bones? Having seen it for myself, it's heartbreaking.

Gem hugged me so hard I thought I'd break a rib myself. She was chuffed and I got that warm, fuzzy feeling again. I mean, I was guilty of violently butt-buffing her so it was the least I could do really. And then Gem gave us a present each for being her girls. It was my second Tiffany box that year, but this one meant a hundred million per cent more to me. She got each of us a necklace with a silver disc engraved with our first initial. As me, Brooke and Gem huddled in a circle crying, the make-up girls ruined the moment moaning about our mascara. I'm not being funny, but if they hadn't used waterproof they only had themselves to blame. It was going to get a whole lot more emotional.

Actually, it got more heated than emotional. You remember I told Gem she should just let us choose our own coral dresses? I'd assumed our interpretations couldn't be that different considering the bridesmaid theme. Turned out I was so wrong. When Gem saw us all lined up together, she flipped. Obviously I had my Fifties-style taffeta coral dress on. Brooke had gone for a coral bodycon dress from CelebBoutique which stopped just short of her crotch. Emily had a long strapless dress with a black sash beneath the bust. Karen and Paula had clearly consulted each other and were wearing identical dresses which were one-shouldered and floaty, almost like baby dolls. We'd all gone for above the knee except for Emily, so that looked strange for a start. Though some of us really shouldn't have gone above the ankle, if I'm to be honest. We looked like we'd escaped from rehab for people with an addiction to coral.

Since I'd already been handy with the thread and needle, I said to Gem we should just hack the length off Emily's dress so we'd all sort of look similar. I mean, Gem only had herself to blame for not checking the dresses before the big day, but I suppose what with the cheating and the wrist thing, she'd had a lot on her mind. Despite Emily's protests, Gem let me loose on her. The hem wasn't quite straight, but I'm not a pro, am I? We'd all have to make do.

Our squabbles were silenced as soon as we laid eyes on Gemma in her dress complete with veil, tiara, Gina shoes, the bling sling and the bouquet. She'd gone for hair down and loosely curled, one side pinned up with a coral flower to match us lot. Now, I don't want to brag, because I always source proper amazing fairytale dresses, but I'd outdone myself with Gem's wedding dress. You can't go wrong with a Wang. It had a classic tight bodice with what some would call a 'meringue' skirt, but, professionally, I would call it an asymmetric cascade of layers.

Now, I'm going to get a lot of haters when I say this, but short girls don't look good in meringue dresses. I'm sorry the truth hurts, but I've seen a lot in my time. If you're only as high as the dress is wide, then you're going to look like a giant snowball. But at five foot eight, Gem had been born for the meringue. The entire dress looked like it had been dipped in lace, but the floaty gazaar overlay had actually been hand-painted with a lace design which looked way more delicate than frumpy old lace. It didn't even need crystallization because the design caught the light with every twist and turn. The sweetheart neckline also had a little ruffled corsage perched on one side. It looked uncomplicated until you got up close and saw it was brimming with drama, just like Gem. Most importantly, it looked proper expensive. I mean, it should have cost £3,000, but Gem paid nowhere near that.

She just sparkled from top to toe, and I've got to admit, Ryan's training sessions had paid off. Not counting Marilyn, there was only one show pony in town today.

✳

Only a big fat Essex wedding would have a red carpet leading up to the church doors. They'd had to pin it down with rocks, though, which had really brought the glam factor down. Gem's dad, Derek, hadn't been allowed at the house so he'd had to meet Gem at the church. Let's just say Linda has major issues with her ex-husband that none of us will ever know about but them. So there was already a bit of tension as Derek walked his youngest down the aisle with Linda giving him dagger eyes, but it got worse when Gemma lifted her veil.

It should be a beautiful moment when the bride first sees the groom, but instead Gem goes, 'Oh my God, what the fuck happened to your nose, Grant?'

Now I looked, it was so obvious – he had this bloodied dent on the bridge of his nose.

'Babe, don't worry about it. It was just a little accident from last night,' he said.

Gemma did look a bit worried, but then stayed focused on the mission – get a ring on it. I won't bore you with the service, but the vicar outed Grant for crying during the rehearsals, which so wasn't cool. Then, as he carried on talking about the love he'd witnessed between Grant and Gem, I heard Grant's mum whisper really loudly, 'The bastard's trying to make him cry again,' which everyone heard, including the vicar. Awkward. And you know that bit where the vicar goes, 'Do you promise to stay faithful to Gemma.' I was literally boring a hole into the back of Grant's head. He seemed to say the words with all sincerity, but he started tugging at his collar during that bit, so he clearly felt the pressure. When they were pronounced man and wife, the whole place erupted with clapping, stamping and whooping. Mr and Mrs Sweet had finally arrived.

It was all systems go after that. Gem and Grant got driven off in a vintage Silver Ghost Rolls-Royce, which was pure class. Meanwhile, we got shoved in the back of Derek's car, although it was an acceptable BMW. He always goes, 'Call me Del,' but I never want to. He thinks he's a proper wheeler-dealer but I refuse to give him the Del accolade. Always Derek.

When we got to the reception in Stapleford, Gemma and Grant were having their photo taken next to this gorgeous green MG with a white ribbon on its bonnet.

'What's all this about, then?' I said to Gemma as soon as I got over to her.

'Grant's bought me this car as a wedding present,' she screamed.

'You're joking? Are you being serious?'

'One hundred per cent, and check out the number plate.'

I walked round to the front and there it was: SW33T. I didn't want to say, but it looked like 'Sweat' from where I was standing.

'Oh my God, Grant, I can't believe you done this for

Gem. I'd have married you if I'd known this was part of the deal,' I said.

'Sorry, ladies, I'm now officially off the market. You all had your chance but you'll have to wait till Gem pops her clogs now.'

'Oh, charming,' Gem said, whacking him with her bouquet.

And the thing is, it wasn't really a surprise because we all knew Grant could afford it. His parents were swimming in cash, which had been a major source of anger as far as this wedding was concerned. Grant's parents hadn't contributed a penny towards it. I'm not kidding you, and just to rub salt in the wound they were all tanned from the £10K world cruise they'd just got back from. Brooke kept telling Grant that he should put in the speech, 'A massive thanks to Gem's three parents, and zero thanks to my own,' but that would have been a bit much. So Grant had pumped a lot of his own money into this day, but he could easily spare it judging by his wedding gift to his new wife. It really took the edge off the fact that he'd deformed his face for his wedding day. All he'd say was that he'd been at Sugar Hut the night before and he'd got home at 4 a.m. Who does that nine hours before they're meant to be stood at the altar? Him and his nose, her and her arm . . . they looked a right pair.

The photo stuff went on for quite a long time and I kept getting called back, so champagne had barely grazed my lips at this wedding. It was my own fault because I'd made Marilyn look too cute, so the photographer got a bit trigger-happy with my little guy. Like, there was one of him in the driving seat of the MG, one of him poking out from under Gem's wedding dress, and, my favourite, one of him lying on his back with his legs open surrounded by all the bridesmaids' bouquets. That was the money shot and it was just begging to be turned into a canvas.

When our modelling duties were done, I had to make up for lost time. I swear I finished a glass of fizz every five minutes. It's like water to me. We spied Brooke and Charlie canoodling under a tree in the garden, and I got to say, I didn't feel any rage. If you're up front with people, it turns out you can talk the rage out of your system. Who knew? And the safety word was totally working. I'd only had to Minge her five times since the hen do. I didn't want to do that for the rest of our lives, but we needed boundaries in these early days. I mean, if I was still doing that on Brooke and Charlie's wedding day, perhaps then you could accuse me of having denial issues. But you got to ease your way into these weird situations or it gets too much, right?

I got to say Charlie looked pretty hot in his best man gear. I think that must have been the suit fetish rearing its head again, but the waistcoat and tails were really doing it for me. I honestly don't still have a thing for him.

I find line-ups at a wedding a weird thing. I'd already spent the morning with Gem and her parents, I'd talked to Grant loads and I'd never ever met Grant's parents. None of us could think of a word to say. They should do away with these silly formalities because it's such a downer to a wedding day. But right at the end of the line there was one joy, and that was Gem's Nana Lily. I love this woman to death. It's not often you get a nan in the line-up, but like I've said, Gem's family are like the Mafia and Nana Lil is the matriarch of the Cox clan. Like, I'm a bit scared of her, but she's inspiring too. Her and my nan are as thick as thieves because they're both East End girls and got the same ideals. Proper no-nonsense grafters, but they know how to have a good time.

I see all this stuff about old people being ignored and lonely, but I honestly don't think this is the case in Essex. People make out Nanny Pat's this rare find, but I'm telling you, we genuinely respect our nans here and they're at the heart of every Essex family. Although my nan's not out in the clubs like Nanny Pat seems to be. Why's she always down Sugar Hut when she should be at home in her slippers? Anyways, respecting your nan is a beautiful thing, and I've seriously learnt a thing or two off the old girls. Nana Lil was on form when I finally reached her. She goes, 'Darlin', you look beautiful. Vera's coming later, ain't she?'

'Course, Nan wouldn't miss a knees-up with you. Look at you all scrubbed up nice in your fancy dress,'

I said, and I wasn't lying. She has an amazing figure for a 77-year-old. Four years older than Nanny Pat, but she's a proper glam nan. Then she whispered to me, 'I'm glad today's gone ahead, but if Grant puts one foot wrong, he'll have me to answer to.'

Oh my God, she can be proper menacing. I hope she hadn't whispered this to *everyone* at the end of the line-up.

※

By the time we sat down for the wedding 'breakfast' in the late afternoon, I was hammered. I'd missed all the canapés because of the photos, and I'd been down-ing champagne and Pimm's for two hours solid. I don't think I've ever eaten at a wedding while sober. Why do people spend money feeding their guests when a bag of chips would do? The only thing I remember about lunch was me and Ryan having a right old barney because he wouldn't fill up my wine glass, which resulted in me knocking over a bottle of red on the girls opposite us. We weren't popular.

And at the next table, Gem's Auntie Carol (you can tell she's Paula's mum, and I don't mean that in a good way), kept crying and running off to the toilets. I don't know what that was all about, but sitting next to her ex-husband must have had something to do with it. Honestly, I don't think Gem put a lot of thought into the dynamics of her seating plan. I mean, me and Ryan had been separated from the others and seemed to be on this weird singles table. It would have been alright if she'd put some eye candy there for us, but it was disappointing. One guy never said a word to me except to introduce himself and then he just stared at me the whole time. What a fucking freak. Had to have been one of Grant's mates. Then we got talking to this nice-looking bloke on Ryan's left who looked twenty-five but talked like he was forty-five, banging on about house prices in West Essex and the minute details of his dull job. We only realized he was height deficient too when we all stood up to toast the bride. Me and Ryan actually spat our drink out in shock. Seriously, his upper body was deceptively normal, but I'd never seen such short legs. He must do a lot of talking to women when sat down. I'm telling you, there's something in the bloody Essex water.

Talking of toasting people, the speeches were interesting, to say the least. Gem's dad decided to reveal his current inner monologue instead of preparing a speech. It was basically a ramble of put-downs aimed at Gem's mum, and he didn't exactly praise Gemma either. It's people like him who make me thankful to have Don Fox as a father. She should have got her step-dad to do it, but Gemma didn't want to rock the boat. I honestly don't think Derek would have cared, since he clearly had major issues. As Nan said, he could turn milk he's so sour. I felt relief when Grant stood up and ended Derek's rant by taking the microphone off him. The mood was awkward, but as soon as Grant started his speech, everyone forgot about Gem's arsehole of a dad. If anything, it went the other way and all got a bit emotional.

'I just wanted to say, Mum and Dad, I know I've made life difficult for you sometimes, but thanks for sticking by me,' he said, stopping to clear his throat. 'Things looked like they were going downhill after school, but you never said nothing. Just gave me your unconditional support, so thank you.' (No mention of their lack of financial support.) 'I also wanted to thank my new family, the Coxes, who basically sorted this whole reception for us. The day I showed up here as Gem's boyfriend, they welcomed me into their home like their own flesh and blood.'

His voice wobbled, the tears started to roll and then he suddenly blurted out the words 'Jelly Tots'. It was fucking weird, like he had Tourette's or something. Everyone in the marquee started murmuring. Then he went, 'Sorry, Charlie told me to use a trigger word if I started getting emotional, and you can't get upset if you think about Jelly Tots . . .' His voice trailed off as he realized he'd lost his audience.

'Anyway, what I am trying to say is this. Linda and her husband Allan have been there for us through thick and a lot of thin, so while you've embraced me as family today, there's no need because you already made me feel a part of it eight years ago. Fuck it, Jelly Tots.'

It went on like this for another ten minutes with him Jelly-Totting all over the shop. I suppose he'd just used my safety word technique, but I never had to say Minge in front of two hundred people. Then he goes, 'I never truly knew how much I loved Gemma until she came back from Marbs with one arm. It made me realize that I'd be inconsolable if anything happened to her. Like, I pictured a world without Gem in it and it wasn't a world worth living in. Shit, Jelly Tots. Gem, you've never looked more stunning than you look today, and I just want to thank you for choosing to spend the rest of your life with me. Jelly Tots.'

Oh my days, I was sobbing it up big time. Jelly Tots actually became a really moving word after a while. That was until I found out from Charlie that it was a reference to some filth that had happened in Amsterdam with a pole dancer. I said, spare me the details, hun. Ignorance is bliss sometimes.

So while Grant's speech had us reaching for the tissues, Charlie's speech had everyone on the floor. He didn't even need to mention the handcuffed dwarf. Turns out not only had Grant asked Charlie to be his best man before he'd even asked Gem to marry him, but he'd also confirmed beforehand what weekend the boys could do the stag on. Gemma properly kicked off. She smacked Grant round the head with her good hand and went, 'You fucking pig.' Awww, we witnessed their first marital fight. I wonder if Charlie had asked Grant to be his best man when we were going out? Do all blokes secure them early like this?

Somehow during the speeches I'd managed to sober up a bit, but Ryan had gone the other way. When I saw he'd been drinking rosé wine, that explained it all. He can't take it. He's fine on red and white, but rosé sends him doolally. We all left the marquee so they could fix it up for the night, but Brooke had to help me drag Ryan out because he was just being irritating. And then my cousin Russ rocked up with Rob. Weirdly, Gem had agreed to pay them to DJ that night. I didn't know they could DJ let alone had the equipment, so I was proper unsure about that decision, but Gem couldn't resist their mates' rates. Russ claimed he just had to play songs off his iPod, but surely it's more complicated than that or we'd all being doing it?

Anyways, it was once the music started pumping that the true dramas unfolded. For starters, my family showed up for the evening do, even my little Lola, who had come dressed as Cinderella. Interesting outfit choice. Gemma had insisted on it because she said they were like her second family. Who was I to stop her? Nan had really pushed the boat out with a pink dress. I swear she looked like Jackie Kennedy. Me and Gem are always praying we've inherited our nans' genes. When they go to bridge nights, those two pull all the lads (what's left of them).

But as they arrived, I saw Gem's dad drive away.

I asked where he was off to and Gem went, 'He said he needs to pop home to feed the dog.' Seemed feasible. His loss, because he missed out on Gem's first dance with Grant. I can never remember anyone's first dance so don't ask, but halfway through it, Gem held out her unbroken hand to her step-dad and they danced the rest of the song while Grant grabbed Linda. Allan was chuffed to bits and Linda nearly fell out of her dress when Grant dipped her. It was a beautiful moment.

I gave my family the once-over to make sure no one was up to no good. Tasha and Tony were being quite affectionate with each other, which was a first. Jake was trying to chat up Emily, which was expected. At one point he came over to me and yelled in my ear, 'The birds fucking love it when you get them a drink. But it's all free! Kudos without the expense!' Don't know if you can tell, but Jake hasn't been to a lot of weddings. Nan was stood by the buffet table which hadn't even been laid out yet. She's always one step ahead, that one. And then Jackie and Don were dominating the dance floor as usual. Even though I was livid that Mum had nicked my unworn Grecian white dress from Karen Millen, I couldn't be mad at her because she looked so beautiful. I felt proper proud, if I'm to be honest, but I did wonder if she was allowed to wear white to a wedding. Aren't there rules? No matter, things like that don't bother Gemma.

And things got a bit tense between me and Gem's

sister. I was stood outside the marquee with Mum and Lola early on in the evening when Karen came out all guns blazing. Proper tanked-up. She goes to me, 'What the fuck are you doing out here?'

'Talking to my family, if you must know,' I replied.

'You are unbelievable. Gemma's in there dancing all alone. Call yourself a bridesmaid?' she said, all manic. Despite the Botox, even Mum was able to raise her eyebrows in astonishment at this little outburst. I wasn't going to stand for that, so I played the emotional guilt card.

'Listen, Lola asked if I could take her to the toilet, so that's what I'm doing.'

'I don't care if Lola needs the toilet. Get back in there and start dancing,' Karen yelled.

Now she'd properly riled me, so I just stormed in there to find shit-loads of people dancing. I honestly don't think Karen could see straight any more. Then she comes up to me ten minutes later and goes, 'Look how many people I got on the dance floor.' She's so screwy. Since when did bridesmaiding get so competitive? And since when was forcing people to dance on my list of duties?

I wasn't really enjoying the dancing either, because you know that staring man from my table? He was stood on the edge of the floor nursing a pint and properly eyeballing me. Maybe that pulling technique works wherever he's from, but in Essex, that's considered creepy. I was desperate to get out of his gaze, so I went up to Gemma and said, 'Karen's being so nuts. I'm actually too scared to stop dancing in case she has a go at me again,' and Gemma replied, 'Babe, why do you think I've been dancing for the last half-hour? I just want to go get a drink. If she doesn't chill out, we're going to fall out.'

When Karen wasn't watching, we both made a run for it. About an hour later, I caught Karen outside texting on her phone. So I thought, let's see how *she* likes it, and went, 'Oi, what the fuck you doing out here? The dance floor's empty,' and she goes, 'I'm sexting, aren't I?'

She'd well and truly outdone me because I had no answer to that. You can't compete with a sexting mentalist.

If all this merriness wasn't enough, I then had to contend with a molestation. I was stood on the side of the dance floor innocently taking pictures of Ryan making a drunken twat of himself when somebody grabbed my bum. And I mean a proper handful of left cheek. You know the staring guy? Surprisingly, it wasn't him. I turned to see Charlie walking off. Can you believe that? See, that's the sort of proof I'm talking about when I say he's still into me. I'm honestly not being arrogant! And since he didn't stick around to get my reaction, we can only assume he knew he'd done wrong and it was the hand of alcohol that had done it. I mean, he's only human, so I don't blame him for being tempted, but it put me in yet another moral fix. In the end, I decided never to mention this to Brooke, as what good could it do? If I'm to be honest, it had done a lot of good for me, though, because I suppose I always want Charlie to fancy me. Is that so wrong?

Just as I was soaking up this exquisite feeling, Brooke came running up to me. For a second I thought she'd seen and wanted to have it out with me.

'You got to come into the house with me. Gem's refusing to come back in,' she said.

'What's going on?'

'Her dad's not returned and her nan's just told her why,' she replied. Did I mention Nana Lil is a right old stirrer? We went up to Gem's old bedroom to find her sobbing face down on her bed.

'Just one day – all he had to do was be a dad to me for one day,' she wailed. Nana Lil was sat there rubbing her back and going, 'Men are all the same, darlin'. Don't let him ruin your evening.'

Derek is actually Lil's son, but he's hardly her favourite, which is probably why she blew the whistle on him. Basically, Derek hadn't gone back to feed the dog, he'd gone back to his 'fancy-piece' in their village and now he was too drunk to come back. More like he was too busy getting his end away. It was a horrible thing to have done, and even though Gemma knows what her dad's like, I knew she'd find an excuse for him as usual. He doesn't even send her birthday cards, that's how bad it is. She's always hopeful, but he always disappoints. I can't blame her for having expectations, though, because girls can't help idolizing their dads, can they?

The only solution was to get Grant to step up and start acting the husband. And to give him credit, once we got him there he managed to say all the right things and even made her smile. As I sat there watching them together, I felt a pang of jel. She was in so much pain, but there he was to pick her up and make her feel better. It was something I wanted for myself, but not, if you know what I mean?

I went and got Gem a glass of champagne. Then me and Brooke fixed Gem's make-up and made Nana Lil get back to the party. She'd done quite enough damage. The bling sling had gone awry too, so I had to do some on-the-spot alterations. It was actually pretty nice having some downtime with the bride and groom. Don't you just find you never spend any time with them at weddings, which sort of defeats the point of a wedding, right? I think I'll have a much more intimate affair, somewhere hot and on a beach. Maybe the Maldives.

Just to give me a reality slap, I heard my phone go off. It was another message from Jamie asking if I wanted to come to some party in Shoreditch next weekend. I wasn't really feeling it, so I just ignored him for the meantime. I wasn't being horrible, it's just that you got to let some replies develop gradually over time like a fine wine, otherwise they come out all acidic. I needed to sleep on it and be sober.

Russ turned out to be an alright DJ, although he was shit at taking requests. Every time I went up, he either didn't have it or wouldn't play it. I pointed out that *everyone* loves 'Come On Eileen', but he said he wouldn't be seen dead playing that. I'm not being funny, but he's hardly going to get anywhere in the DJ world if that's his attitude. Anyways, before I knew it, he was playing their last song. What gives with weddings being over so quickly? Unfortunately, they'd chosen 'All Night Long' by Lionel Richie. I envy all of you who still find joy in that uplifting melody because Ryan has tainted it for ever.

So the music started and a circle gathered round the newly-weds. All good so far. But then I spotted Ryan taking his shoes off. He then put a shoe on each hand and started dancing in the circle with Gem and Grant. We were absolutely pissing ourselves, and each time Ryan tried to get out of the circle, Charlie shoved him back into the middle. Eventually he stayed there and just happily played the trumpet with his shoe-hands.

It was when Ryan started with the shouting that it stopped being so funny. At the top of his voice he yelled, 'The marriage is a sham, the marriage is a sham,' over and over. Lionel was singing 'jambo jumbo' so loud that no one seemed to hear Ryan's outburst, so I ran into the circle, pushed Charlie out the way and got Ryan out of there.

'What you playing at, babe?' I asked. Ryan just stared back with a blank expression. 'Listen, I can't talk to you with your shoes on your hands, hun,' I said, pulling them off him.

He grabbed his shoes back and scurried back into the circle, skidding into Gemma and Grant as he went. As he regained his balance, he yelled, 'The marriage is a sham,' right in Gem's face. Her face dropped and she stopped dead in her tracks and looked angrily at Grant. I had to use every ounce of strength to drag Ryan out of the marquee entirely, and Brooke wasn't far behind.

'You've done it now,' I said, furious with him.

'People got to be honest if they like a bit of cock, yeah?' he said.

'Who, Gemma or Grant?' I said, proper confused now.

'He means your Tony,' Brooke said, interrupting.

'What you talking about? Hun, what's going on?'

Brooke grabbed Ryan's iPhone and brought up his Grindr profile. Right at the top, there was a bloke called 'IG8 Straight', and he was twenty metres away according to this. Brooke went on to his profile and there was Tony's big old moon face staring back at me.

'What's this all mean?'

'The marriage is a sham,' Ryan repeated. Since he was talking like a crack-head, it was left to Brooke to explain.

'You remember the Duke of Essex Polo, yeah? That's when Ryan first saw him with Tasha. You know this bloke who's been jizzing on him in the showers at Virgin Active? That's Tony.'

'You're kidding me?'

'That's not everything. Ryan also met him up town after work once. When I say they met up town, I mean they met in Liverpool Street station's toilets. Apparently it's rife in there. Let's just say it was a mutually beneficial meeting.'

'I don't believe this. Why's he not told me any of this?'

'Because he didn't want to be the one tearing up your family. You know loads of blokes do this sort of shit but it don't make them a bad husband or father? Like, he could be bi and just a bit confused, right?'

'So Ryan's been sat on this bombshell for two whole months?'

'Becs, you should have seen him at the polo. He didn't know what to do with himself. I was the one who told him not to say anything.'

'Well no wonder he's so off his face now. He wasn't built to contain secrets. So hold up, has Ryan spoken to Tony?' I asked.

'Yeah, they had a little tête-à-tête when Tony got here.'

'I geddit now – so that's why the dicksplash is being all cosy with Tasha. He's fucking scared, isn't he?'

'So what you going to do, babe?' asked Brooke.

'I'm not going to a piggin' thing. It's nothing to do with me. If Tony were having a full-on emotional affair with someone, then I'd have to get involved, but looks to me like he's just fooling around for the moment.'

Don't get me wrong, this was a shock, but I suppose my gut instinct had always told me Tony was up to no good. I mean, he couldn't seriously have been watching *all* those sport programmes. Darts, I ask you? But I'd make the call when or if I needed to step in. And I'd be confronting Tony if I did, not Tasha. I'm no grass. At the end of the day, it was my little Lola that was in the forefront of my mind. She's a well happy kid, so why rock her world? In a way, it was a good thing he'd been caught out because now he knew he was playing a very dangerous game. I wanted Tony to feel the fear and not think he could take my sister for a mug. He'd have to make up his own mind about where his loyalties lay. Right now a more urgent matter needed to be dealt with, so I had to leave Brooke outside with Ryan. I was very aware that Gemma would be thinking the worst right now.

The music had stopped long ago and everyone was gradually filtering out of the marquee. Gem was hugging some old dear and smiling away, but as soon I got up to her the mask slipped right off.

'What was all that about? What's Ryan mean?' she said, grabbing me with her good arm and looking all urgent.

'Calm the passion, hun,' I said. 'He's so drunk he doesn't know what he's saying. But let me tell you this much. It's not your marriage that's the sham. He means some other marriage.'

'Are you lying to me?'

'Swear on my nan's life, it was aimed at some other poor sods. I can't really talk about it,' I said, ending it there. I normally tell her everything, but this seemed a bad story to tell someone on their wedding day. I couldn't say 'our old school friend's sucked off my sister's husband'. I wanted her to have a hundred per cent faith in marriage on today of all days.

She knew not to question me further and just went, 'Thank fuck for that. Honestly, babe, I couldn't take another personal drama today.'

'Tell me about it. But it's been fun though, hasn't it?' I said hopefully.

'Most amazing day of my life, babe,' she said. 'Thanks for getting me through everything earlier. He's a shit, and I know it.'

'Hun, no need to thank me, it's my job. And check this out,' I said, waving my iPhone at her. 'I filmed Ryan dancing with his shoes on his hands. How many hits do you reckon we'll get when I upload it on YouTube?'

'Oh my God, amazing! Sweet revenge is ours. He did take down that one of me and the stripper, didn't he?'

'Yeah, course he did,' I replied, although I really couldn't be sure. He told me the one of me falling into a bush had been taken down, but had it fuck. Ryan's actually going to kill me when he sees that I've detailed the most humiliating episode in his life like this, but it happened – I got video evidence and I got witnesses, so sue me.

Ryan was in no fit state to go home alone so I decided he was coming back with the Foxes that night. I'd seen Jake snogging Emily in a corner, and, if I knew my brother, Emily wouldn't be needing the bed at mine. When I finally found Ryan again, he was sat in Gemma's parents' house with Marilyn, scribbling in the sodding Guest Book. I grabbed it off him but it was too late. He'd written under each heartfelt message the exact same thing. For instance, one of them went like this: 'My darling Gem and Grant, Congratulations on your wedding day. You've made your old nan very proud and I hope you have as many happy years together as me and your granddad did. He would have loved today so much but I'm sure he was watching over us all. Love you very much, Nana Lily . . . *And Ryan, your favourite gay*.' If anything, Gem's granddad would have been turning in his urn, because each message was accompanied by a drawing of a giant cock, and he hadn't missed a single page either.

I threw the pen across the room in despair. I couldn't believe Brooke had left him alone after all he'd done that evening. There was nothing we could do now, so I pulled him up, stuck a sleepy Marilyn under my arm and walked them to the waiting minibus. En route he even tried to stick his tongue down my throat, so that just shows how gone he was. Ryan, that is, not Marilyn. I shoved both of them in between Nana Vera and Dad for safe-keeping while I went and said my goodbyes to Gem and Grant in the marquee. I found Brooke snogging the face off Charlie in there too. Typical. Isn't it the law that all the bridesmaids get some action, and not from a gay? Proper disappointing.

I got back to the bus to find my dad with his arm around Ryan. Ryan was sobbing away while Nan tried to console him. 'You'll find yourself a nice man some day, darlin',' she said to him. 'These things take time. I'm a bit psychic and I'd say your fella was just on the horizon.'

I noticed Tony shift uncomfortably in the back. It must all have felt a bit too close to home for him. And I reckon he knew I knew because he didn't take the piss out of me once on the way home. It was quite a peaceful journey back with Ryan's soft whimpering in the background. It gave me a chance to reflect on all that had happened. It then occurred to me that something *hadn't* happened.

'Oh my God, did Gemma throw her bouquet?' I said suddenly.

'Brides don't seem to do that any more,' Emily said. 'They like to keep their wedding flowers.'

'That is so fucking selfish,' I said, feeling outraged.

'What about the rest of us? They're jinxing all our marriage prospects if they're hogging all the bouquets.'

'People make such a fuss about their weddings, these days,' Nan chipped in. 'I got married, then I went straight on my honeymoon. I didn't care much about keeping flowers.'

'That's what I'm saying – why are brides so fucking precious these days? I would have given the flowers back if she'd asked.'

'Becs, have you had quite a bit to drink?' Mum said, interrupting me.

'Yeah, maybe,' I replied. I rested my head against the window and took some time out. No one likes the drunk ranter at the end of the evening.

18

The Only Way is a WEG
Wedding Day

The best bit about a wedding is the gossip the day after. Although, Ryan wasn't exactly the most chatty person the next morning. I woke up to the sound of him hurling into what I hoped was my toilet. Much to his irritation, I was feeling kinda perky. I wanted to find out what Ryan had said to Tony, but he wouldn't come out the bathroom so I left him to it and walked over to the parents.

As soon as I walked into the living room, Mum and Dad stopped talking.

'I see, I see, keeping secrets, are we?'

'Never from you, Princess . . . I thought you was Jake,' Dad said.

'What you whispering about, then?'

'Just about how busy Jake was last night,' Mum replied, taking a furtive sip of her tea.

'C'mon, and the rest . . .' I said, having to lead them into the goss.

'Well, you know who's in his room right now. But Nan saw him snogging Cleo at one point,' said Dad.

'And then I saw him snogging one of the bar girls,' added Mum. 'I really don't know about him. He needs to have his heart broken and see how he likes it.'

'So that makes Emily his third victim?' I said, doing some amazing maths. 'I just don't get how he stops the other girls from finding out. He must have sensors in his back or something.'

'Do something dangerous every day, that's what he says,' Dad said, brimming with pride. Dad totally encourages this Casanova behaviour, but when I told Dad and Jake what had happened with Ben (and I gave them the clean version of events), they both exploded. Such double standards. Don't get me wrong, I admire Jake for grabbing life by the balls, but I wish he was more respectful towards my people.

That afternoon we returned to the scene of the crime, as Gem's parents had put on a post-wedding barbecue. Miraculously, I'd managed to get Ryan moving and drove him back to his flat to change. Marilyn was forced to sit on his lap on the way, but I told him if he puked on my baby, I was dropping them both off at the doggy day spa. I put a couple of sick bags in the glove compartment just in case.

Gem and Grant literally pounced on the SLR as soon

as we came up the drive. I could see it in their eyes – they wanted me to feed them a few spoonfuls of scandal – so I told them about Jake's hat-trick just to keep them going. They were loving it.

I got Ryan out the car and he held on to me like an old man. You would not have thought the boy was a personal trainer. I sat him down and sorted him out with a pint of orange and lemonade. You cannot beat that drink when you're hanging, but he needed a sugar hit too so I grabbed a plate of Chocolate Fingers. 'C'mon, have just one. Everybody loves a Finger,' I said, but even that didn't get a rise out of him. He needed more time before he could give me the gritty details, so I left him to recover.

I tried having a go at the barbecue with Grant for a bit, but all the sausages kept falling through the grill. Who designed these things, I ask you? I gave up for everybody's sake and decided to join Gem, Brooke and Charlie, who were now sat with Ryan. Charlie wouldn't look me in the eye at first, so he clearly had a guilty conscience. Ryan was looking even more pathetic thanks to Nana Lil, who had now wrapped a blanket round him.

'What do you look like, hun?' I said.

'I'm dying, leave me be,' Ryan murmured weakly. He really was milking it. But once everyone's stories started flying back and forth, Ryan's strength visibly returned. We always call him the Gossip Gollum because he gets this wild, fevered look when he hears scandals, but now, with that blanket round his head, he genuinely looked the part. He was literally bouncing on his seat as he drank up our precious morsels.

So it turned out Gem did have it out with Karen in the end because of the 'forced fun' she was inflicting on all her guests. That ended in Karen crying, which is why she went off sexting to make herself feel better. And then she tried to walk back home to Epping from Stapleford Abbotts even though she was staying at her mum's that night, so they had to sedate her with a valium. So glad this side of her never came out on the hen do. I've not been trained to cope with sexting single mums.

Then Gem revealed the reason why her Auntie Carol had kept crying. Apparently she said her table was too far from the head table, which she thought was disrespectful considering she was Gem's godmother and mother of a bridesmaid. What a prima donna. Honestly, Gem's family are something else. They've got this pecking order that goes on there, and sometimes one aunt gets jealous of another and then Nana Lils has to step in and sort the lot of them out like she's the Godfather. What a blooming headache. I still say it was not a good idea to stick her next to her ex-husband though.

Once we'd dissected Gem's family dramas, Brooke told us (in a totally pass-agg way) that she couldn't find

Charlie when the taxi turned up and had ended up going home alone. He was then found by Gem's step-dad asleep on the lawn at 2 a.m. Allan said that with the amount of grass and shit on Charlie's jacket it was now a genuine Moss Bros suit. It was a dad-gag worthy of Don Fox.

Talking of my family, it was while we were mid-debrief that Jake rocked up with Emily in tow. He'd texted me earlier to make sure Cleo wasn't there, and then he managed to show up just as food was served. So jammy. Anyways, he offered a *very* valuable contribution to all this and revealed the mystery of Grant's dented nose. Turns out Jake had been at Sugar Hut on Friday night too and he'd seen a fight break out in the street where a bloke ripped a shirt off another bloke's back. When he got a closer look, he saw that the now shirtless man was Grant and he was now charging head first in to this other guy's crotch. Grant loves his clothes, so I can see why he would have been enraged. I wouldn't like my dress ripped off me. So that's when he did the damage to his nose and then passed out on the street. This is the kind of shit that *really* goes down at Sugar Hut, but I think TOWIE should stick to filming Gemma's Love-Struck singles nights and Joey's Reem Sundays.

While Grant was still busy at the barbecue, I asked Gemma the question we all wanted to know: had they consummated the marriage? As per usual, the answer was no. I've started up my own personal poll to find out if anyone has sex on their wedding night, and so far, I've had one hundred per cent negative answers. It's a proper depressing statistic, but one day I hope to meet one wife who has put out on her wedding night. Obviously I only ask this question to newly-weds. I'm not interested in finding out the answer from Mum or Nan. That's information I could do without. I suppose Gem did have a broken wrist, so I'll let her off.

That bloody wrist of hers had ruined a lot of things, including her honeymoon. Gem told us that they'd had no choice but to postpone it, which was proper sad. They were meant be going on this cruise for two months, the same one Grant's parents had been on. It sounded so amazing, but there's no way she could go off for that long, especially since the pins were coming out in six weeks' time. You wouldn't exactly want to take that contraption to the Seychelles either. So now they were going in the new year and would be having a 'mini-moon' instead. All the time-starved celebs are doing that now. They go away for a few days' holiday after the wedding but have the proper honeymoon when they can fit it into their hectic schedule. What a sad life. So Grant and Gem were flying to Italy for the week instead, which, to be honest, didn't sound much of a hardship.

Just when we thought we were done with the gossip, I remembered Ryan. He'd been awful quiet, but I told him, it's not all take, take, take, you know. Reluctantly, he dished the details. He showed me Tony's profile on Grindr so I could have a proper look this time. 'IG8 Straight' was apparently 'married bi-curious' and he was a 'top' who was up for anything 'except barebacking'. I was glad to hear it, but it's strange what you find comforting when reading your brother-in-law's profile on Grindr. 'Hundred per cent prime Essex beef?' You are having a laugh.

My main concern was that he was putting Tasha's health at risk, but at least he practised safe sex. Ryan said they'd met in Virgin Active and had been 'horsing around' in the showers a few months back. Ryan was kindly toning it down for me because I honestly never want to picture Tony doing anything sexual. And yes, they'd met up at Liverpool Street station one day after work, and then it stopped as soon as he saw him at the polo. Apparently Tony had seen him then but they hadn't spoken. Ryan was really apologetic, especially since he said he didn't even fancy Tony. But it's not like he had anything to be sorry about. It was Tony's own stupid fault for getting in this mess.

We'd just have to see how this played out over the next few months, but believe me, I would be making Ryan monitor his every move. Who knows, maybe it was good for him to explore his gay side. I honestly don't get why people can't be upfront about sexuality these days. Maybe he did love Tasha and just needed a bit of cock sometimes. Who am I to know the inner workings of Tony Crook's tiny mind?

I felt properly exhausted after the afternoon at Gemma's parents. Maybe there's a limit to how much gossip one person can absorb? But as we all kept saying over and over again, 'What a party.' I've been to a few weddings in my time, but an Essex one trumps them all. If Kate and Wills' wedding was half as eventful, I'll be very surprised. I mean, did Pippa Middleton have her bum grabbed by an ex? Did Wills get hammered at a club the night before? Was Harry found unconscious on the lawn of Buckingham Palace at 2 a.m.? Did the Queen grass up Charles for leaving the party to shack up with his fancy-woman? Did a fit aristocrat dance around with his shoes on his hands? I'd like to say no, but if I give it a bit of thought – possibly.

Set Your Sights High

I got to say, I bloody love autumn. Mum says to me, 'I don't know why you love it, it's such a messy season. Leaves everywhere.' But I just feel like I think a lot clearer and I start cooking up plans. It's like that back-to-school feeling where you've wiped the slate clean, you got your new pencil case and you got a fire in your belly.

I mean, you'd have thought after Gemma's wedding I'd be feeling a bit deflated with nothing major to look forward to. Wrong. So much is going on!

Since *The Only Way Is Essex* lot started filming again, I'd say there's more hysteria than ever. Like everyone's going on about where they're going to be and what they know about new characters. It's endless. And the worst culprits are my mum, Cheryl and Sue. Swear to God, Mum's on Twitter now, so she can stalk them and get in the background. They were filming Chloe and Joey down Queens Road at one point and Cheryl sidles up to one of the producers and goes, 'So how can we be in this shot?' and he replies, 'Well they sell swimwear in that shop across the road. Why don't you pop yourself in a bikini and then we'll talk.' Cheryl was beside herself until Mum told her he was taking the piss. I don't know how Cheryl gets on in day-to-day life without Mum's assistance.

And there's been an exciting new development in the world of shopping. What with the opening of West-field in Stratford, I can hop on the Central line and be at the shops in fifteen minutes. I mean, I'll always love Bluewater, but the traffic is a bitch around there. And to be honest, I've always loved that feeling of having shopped up west and being surrounded by shopping bags on the tube ride home, you know what I mean?

When I first heard the Olympics was happening in Stratford, I was like, meh. But as soon as I heard they were building a shopping emporium there, I was all over the place. I was there two days after it opened, and guess who I saw walking around like they owned the place? Only Mark and Arg, aka Marge. No one was taking the blindest bit of notice of them, though. Funnily enough, I saw Mark shopping once before down Carnaby Street. Basically, he had this teenage boy with him who seemed to be carrying all the bags. I'd like to think Mark had taken this kid out for a massive shopping fest, but I think the truth might be that this kid was there to carry Mark's bags. I honestly wouldn't put it past him since Brooke told me she asked for a picture with Mark when he was down Faces recently and he went to her, 'I think I need to start charging,' and she laughed, but he didn't. I think he genuinely might start charging, so watch yourself if you approach him. Since leaving TOWIE, I actually think his head's got bigger. I didn't think it was possible.

And Brooke has appeared in a few scenes in TOWIE which has been proper exciting. Even better, Russ and Rob haven't. So much for their 'we're best friends with Kirk' line. The first scene she did, she was in the audience for Jessica's lingerie catwalk show which happened in Faces. She said she was so hot for Mario she forgot Mark was even there. I love the fact they portrayed them as two rutting stags because it's so true – that much testosterone is genuinely floating around West Essex. Brooke was also in the background for Kirk's Sugar Hut karaoke party which we all could have gone to, but I'm not interested and Gemma didn't want her arm on national television. It's been so long now, I've honestly forgotten what she looks like without her mechanical arm.

Anyways, the best news of all is that Jack Tweed's still not in TOWIE. If that ever happens, that show is dead to me. But I tell you who has been riding the crest of the Essex wave – Jodie Marsh is back on TV and all because she got involved in that body-building malarkey. I can't say I'm a fan of the girl, but you got to admire her tenacity. If you think about it, she was on *Essex Wives*, which was the original Essex documentary a whole decade ago. You got to respect that.

Gemma said to me, 'If you want to get noticed, becoming a body-builder is way more original than getting a boob job.' She makes a good a point.

And just in case you're interested, I'm going to get my own boobs sorted out at Holly House. Even though Brooke says I'm hallucinating, I honestly believe one is drooping more than the other and I can't be having that. Not that anyone's seen me naked recently to check them out. Sorry to say, nothing has occurred with Jamie yet. I fobbed him off because I didn't want to go to Shoreditch, but then I discovered the party was at Shoreditch House. They got a blooming rooftop pool there!

OK, so I'll admit I like him and I promise I'll go on a date with him, but I do think our scenes are totally different. Can you seriously imagine me slumming it at some party in an East End warehouse? I'd have to create my own VIP section out of beer crates or something. I got to stop going over that in my head, though, because nobody got nowhere by thinking too much. I'll just make it somewhere on my turf for the first date. I've been dying to go to Smith's Brasserie in Ongar and it's the kind of place that blokes love. When you see all the flash cars lined up outside on a Saturday night, you get a buzz before you've even stepped in the restaurant.

I think Jamie sees West Essex as this foreign land, so I will happily be his tour guide. And maybe I could take him shopping down Westfield beforehand so he has some nice clothes to wear and then we could burn those shorts?

Thankfully, I haven't heard a word from Ben. I was a bit scared of bumping into him in One9Five for a while, but Charlie assures me that he won't let him in if he sees him. I'm not normally like this with blokes I've slept with, but in the clear light of day, I've decided that Ben was a psychopath. Not in the murderous sense, but I read this article about one recently and Ben totally fitted the criteria. For instance, they're charming and they'll charm your friends and family. They seem like a really good catch because they're obscenely good looking, successful, persuasive, but they're actually morally blind, emotionally bankrupt and don't feel sorry for anything they do.

Now, I get that I've just described a lot of Essex men here, but if I think back to Ben, I knew something wasn't right. I mean, he was proper hunting me, which would make me his prey. How gross is that. I just hope he has fucked off to America now so all WEGs can be safe from his handsome clutches. I feel like I should write to US Immigration to tell them, but what's one more psychopath over there?

Anyways, no matter cos I'm going places. I've been killing it at the wedding fairs and you may have seen me sauntering down the catwalk at a few. I've properly got my swagger back. I saw Lauren Goodger flogging her fake tan down one of the biggest fairs in Brentwood. She's not exactly the greatest advert for her product because she does have an orange tinge. Then again, I doubt she uses the products because looked to me like she'd had a professional spray. I don't know if it goes against trading standards if you falsely claim to be wearing the product you're selling, but I would have thought so.

Then again, who am I to talk, with my lies about our 'celebrity clients'. I swear I'm getting worse because I told one woman Petra Ecclestone had bought her dress from us. I don't even think she lives in the area, but people love to shop where a millionairess shops, right? I don't know if I'll say Chantelle bought her dress from us, even though I've got nothing against arranged marriages. Maybe I've given the girl a hard time, though. I'm only saying that because I went into Vardo the other day and bought this stunning Vivienne Westwood bag. It's gold and shaped like a seashell. What's not to like? It's going to be part of my outfit for the big Essex Fashion Week party at Woolston Manor. Then I got this amazing Ted Baker pink feathered cape to go over my shoulders. I don't care if Dad does say I look like a flamingo. Fashion Week has become such a big deal now, I wouldn't be surprised if it was in *Vogue* sooner or later.

Anyways, all I'm saying is there's a lot of electricity around West Essex at the moment. There always has been, but now there's outsiders with their noses pressed up against the window wanting an invite to the action. I haven't told Tash this yet, but I've got itchy feet and I just feel like now's the time to do something for myself. Don't get me wrong, I'm going to give a hundred per cent to her business, but I want one of my own. I just hope she doesn't feel like I'm abandoning her. Everyone should do what makes them happy, unless it's murdering people or shit like that. And the only way you can do that is by living for yourself and not other people, right?

I'm not even sure what I want to do yet, but I'm sure inspiration will strike while I'm out and about. It usually does, and, like I say, I usually find opportunities fall my way because I'm in the right place at the right time. I mean, how do you think I got to write this book?

Watch and learn, people.